ORIGINAL WRITING

FROM

IRELAND'S OWN

2013

ORIGINAL WRITING

ISBNS
PARENT: 978-1-78237-380-3
EPUB: 978-1-78237-381-0
MOBI: 978-1-78237-382-7
PDF: 978-1-78237-383-4

A CIP catalogue for this book is available from the National Library.

Published by ORIGINAL WRITING LTD., Dublin, 2013
Printed by CLONDALKIN GROUP, Glasnevin, Dublin 11

INTRODUCTION

Ireland's Own, in conjunction with Original Writing, is delighted to bring to readers this fourth Anthology of the winners and other highly commended entries in our annual writing competitions. Our first three books were very well received and this has encouraged us to publish a 2013 edition, and we feel confident this collection will once again be enjoyed.

The stories and memoirs in this book give a good flavour of what can be enjoyed in the Ireland's Own magazine every week, along with many other regular features such as Song Words, Cookery, Health and Lifestyle column, a substantial children's section and our old friends, Miss Flanagan, Cassidy and Dan Conway.

Apart from our regular corps of professional and part-time contributors, Ireland's Own receives a great many unsolicited submissions every week, many of them of a very good standard. We are only able to use a small portion of these but we are constantly reminded of the great hunger there is out there among people who desire to express themselves and commit their ideas to print. Writing has never been so popular and we do try to be sympathetic and encouraging in our approach

We have been running our Annual Short Stories and Memories Writing Competitions for many years, and they attract a very high-standard response. For the past six years we have been supported in this by the self-publishing company, Original Writing, from Dublin, and their backing is greatly appreciated and our partnership with them has again made this anthology possible.

We congratulate the prizewinners and all the other writers included. We thank them all for their help and co-operation with this project and hope they are justifiably proud of the end result. We also compliment the hundreds of others who entered – perhaps you will have better luck in this year's competitions and will make it into the 2014 Anthology.

We specially thank international bestselling author Claudia Carroll for providing us with a foreword for the book; her support and encouragement is greatly appreciated and we feel sure her words will be taken to heart by our writers, and by all those who are anxious to get involved in writing.

We thank former Ireland's Own editors, Gerry Breen and Margaret Galvin, for all their help with the annual competitions. A special word of thanks to Martin Delany, Garrett Bonner, Steven Weekes and all the crew at Original Writing for their expertise and assistance.

We meet a few old friends in this fourth collection, but there are a few others who are being published in a book for the first time and it is very special for them in particular. Inclusion in this anthology is a significant step for all the writers involved; we wish them all future success if they pursue their writing ambitions. Ireland's Own is happy to have played a part in helping you along the way.

Phil Murphy, Monthly Editor
Sean Nolan, Weekly Editor
Ireland's Own

ORIGINAL WRITING

Original Writing Limited ('OW') has had an association with Ireland's Own for a number of years both as sponsor of the magazine's writing competitions and as publisher of the 'Original Writing From Ireland's Own' Over these years there have been many wonderful entries and it was with this in mind that we came up with the idea for the anthology. We would like to take this opportunity to congratulate all of the winners and other authors whose writings are contained in this anthology.

Original Writing Limited is a member of the Original Writing Group of companies which offers outlets for the written word across a number of websites devoted to publishing and creative writing. One of the products offered may be of particular interest to readers of Ireland's Own who also write in their spare time or have family members or friends who write.

OW can now give the writer an opportunity to have his or her work collected in one place and a paperback or hardback of bookshop quality with a full colour cover, produced by OW to distribute to family, friends and colleagues. Page counts can be as low as twelve and orders are accepted from five copies. Prices start at €2.65 per copy. For more information please logon to www.originalwriting.ie

We also run shortwrites.com which is an online writers' resource where you can share your short stories, get feedback and comment on other writers' work. There is also news, events, interviews, reviews, competition information and many other writing resources. Check out the site at: www.shortwrites.com

We also offer websites for writers. Use our simple website builder to create a stylish, affordable and easily manageable online showcase for your work. Just go to www.netwrites.com for more information.

Contact Original Writing Limited at 01-6174834 or info@originalwriting.ie. Further details are also available at www.originalwriting.ie, www.shortwrites.com and www.netwrites.com

FOREWORD

BY CLAUDIA CARROLL

Former Fair City star and now international bestselling author

A VERY WARM welcome to the fourth Ireland's Own anthology of short stories and can I just say what an absolute honour it is to have been asked to write the foreward for it? Huge thanks to the wonderful team, not only at Ireland's Own, but also at Original Writing, for your continued support and encouragement to writers everywhere. You've no idea how much it means and long may your magical tradition of storytelling continue.

Can I also say warm congratulations to all the fantastic writers whose stories are published in this anthology? It's a truly amazing thing, actually seeing something you've written there in black in white and taking its first baby steps out into the world. I'm not a mother, but I imagine it must be the very same feeling a mum gets when she sees her little newborn for the very first time. And I also know that the standard for this year's anthology was incredibly high, so you all deserve to feel proud as punch and to go out and celebrate!

One of the questions I'm often asked is, how come Ireland produces so many writers? You only have to look at bestseller lists everywhere and even the Booker Prize longlist to see how we somehow manage to punch well above our weight internationally. And I think the reason is we're all such incredible talkers. Is there anything we all love more than a good natter? (If you saw the whopping size of my phone bill, you'd see the proof of that!) And when we sit down to write our stories, then something magical starts to leap off the page. You only have to have a flick through this anthology to see what I mean.

I always think a short story is probably the most difficult craft of all to master. Winston Churchill once wrote, 'I'm sorry for the long letter, I didn't have time for a short one!' Easy to see just what he meant, isn't it? A longer story, maybe even one where you've got the luxury to pad it out to a full-length book, is in many ways so much easier to tackle than facing the challenge of distilling your ideas into a short story, with beguiling characters, a gripping story and an ending that lingers. And yet every published writer here has achieved just that, each in a wonderfully unique way.

Massive congratulations once again to you all, may this anthology sell by the truckload and fly off shelves... and long may Ireland's Own and Original Writing continue to soar and fly!

Warmest wishes to everyone and happy reading.

Claudia Carroll.

CONTENTS

COMPETITION WINNERS

A GOOD MOTHER

By Tony McGettigan,
Dublin

Hannah has eventually made the decision to clear out her mother's house, having put it off for the six months since her death. She had been a good mother, but what secrets were lurking in her belongings?

HANNAH HAD postponed this day for as long as possible. During the six months since her mother's death, she had been to check on the house several times but today she was there to start removing, disposing of her mother's "things".

On her drive up to Dublin, she had dismissed any feelings of sadness at the task ahead and focussed instead on the practicalities of getting it done. She parked at the house in the small suburban cul-de-sac, turned off the engine and sat in the protective quiet of the car for a minute, organising herself against memories. A "For Sale" sign had not yet gone up. The house looked abandoned. She got out of the car and walked up the short drive to the front door. She felt calm and at ease.

Their neighbour of many decades, Mrs O'Brien, came out of the adjoining house.

"Is that you, Hannah?" she asked. "I can't see a thing without my glasses, age, you know, and I don't like wearing my glasses. Vanity!"

"How are you, Mrs O'Brien?"

"I'm grand, thank God. I saw the car pulling up and I was wondering if it was you. I just wanted to say hello. Come in for a cup of tea, will you, before you leave."

Mrs O'Brien pushed an imaginary lock of hair from her

forehead with a quick gesture of her right hand and tucked it behind her ear. Hannah smiled at the familiar mannerism.

"Thanks very much. I'll see, if I have time later. I'm starting the clear out today, at long last. I'll be busy. I want to get as much done as possible."

"A sad business. And you have no one with you, to keep you company and help out."

"Well, John, remember John, my brother?, he lives in Cork and my husband has to work. I've taken a few days off myself to get it done. I'll be alright. I've been preparing myself for this for months. I have a system worked out."

"John. I saw him at the funeral. He's looking well. I hadn't seen him since he left home, after college, He hasn't been home much but I recognised him immediately. And he's in Cork?"

"Yes, has been for many years now."

"Ah, how the years fly. It seems such a short time ago since you were all young ones. This cul-de-sac was full of comings and goings and things happening. It's as quiet and still as a graveyard now."

"Yes," Hannah replied and left it at that; she did not want to start recalling the past.

But, Mrs O'Brien said, "I remember John well. He was such a handsome young man. The girls were mad about him. You had your admirers too, lots of them. But you only had eyes for Tom Byrne from . . . where's this he was from . . . he was always rushing for the last bus, after seeing you home."

"Rathmines . . . he was from Rathmines."

"He was mad about you. We all thought you'd marry him, eventually, but you were both so young, very young. Were you even twenty at the time?"

"Yes, we were very young."

Hannah's heart tightened. She did not want to think about Tom Byrne and how deeply they had been in love. How its ending had broken her heart. How, to her surprise, even now, at the mention of his name, she suddenly found her heart still raw and bruised. She was finding it hard to breathe.

"My goodness, I'm amazed you still remember," she

continued, with a casualness she did not feel. "That's, oh, must be twenty five years ago, more even."

"I wonder where he is now. I often think about the young people who grew up in this cul-de-sac, young ones I knew so well. I knew all of you so well, not having my own. You gave the street such life and fun, all those years ago. I often wonder what became of everyone. Ah, the passing of time leaves so much in its wake. I wonder where Tom Byrne is now. Whatever happened to him?"

"He went to London . . . to work . . . I never heard from him after that."

The thing Hannah had wanted to avoid stole over her and began to suffocate her. Memories of herself and Tom Byrne, memories so linked to that house, to that garden, the times she and Tom had lingered in each other's arms, on the seat by the gable end, where it got the sun, and on the back doorstep, an intensity of feeling that had never been experienced again.

"If I can be of any help, just ring on the door," Mrs O'Brien said. "Your mother was a great woman, God rest her, a great woman, a good mother to you and John, taking care of everything on her own, after your father died, and he so young, it was terrible. Do come in before you leave."

Her invitation hardly registered with Hannah, hardly penetrated the swirl of memories that filled her mind, but she replied, "Yes, yes, thanks, I will".

Mrs O'Brien turned and went into her house. Hannah stepped inside her door, closed it softly behind her and drifted into the past.

Life had never been the same after she had finally accepted that Tom was not going to write from London. Oh God, those days and weeks waiting for his letter, months of waiting, years even, before she began to forget. Her mother had been such a comfort, such a support. She had re-assured her many times, admonishing her that she was being ridiculous, that she was too young to understand.

But, why had Tom promised to write, promised so passionately, with longing in his kisses, and then . . . as if their love had never existed. How could he do that? Her mother was right, of course. She was being ridiculous. She thought she had exorcised all that emotion long ago but why then had she looked for him at her mother's funeral, half-hoped for his hand on her arm.

And her husband of ten years beside her at the grave, that good, kind man, who had become her husband, her husband, and ... Hannah straightened her shoulders and breathed deeply until her mind was clear and her customary self-discipline restored. A storm had swept through her but now she was focussed and relaxed again. She went out to the car for the large plastic bags and cardboard boxes that she had brought for the clearance and took them upstairs to her mother's bedroom to begin work.

She was uneasy in her mother's bedroom. In the thirty seven years that she had lived in that house, until her marriage, she had never touched anything in that private room. I must concentrate, she thought. She chose a box for things she might want to keep, mementoes of her mother, jewellery, trinkets, anything at all.

She had been a good mother, who had looked after, protected and guided her, and John, for as long as she could; not easy, not that Hannah knew much about it, not having any children herself, but it couldn't have been easy, her father having died when they were all so young. Mother would have been much younger then than I am now, Hannah thought. She would share the mementoes with John. He would definitely want some although he had always had a difficult relationship with their mother. She opened another box for things that could go to the Vincent de Paul shop and several large bags for things for the waste management centre.

She started with the dressing table. She cleared its top and emptied its drawers quickly and dispassionately. The chest of drawers and bedside cabinets were next. All was neat and tidy. There was nothing of her father anywhere. Her mother was not a hoarder. She opened the wardrobe and began to clear it quickly and deliberately, not thinking of the contents as her mother's clothes. Everything was rolled into bundles, without removing the hangers, and stuffed into plastic bags.

When the hanging rail was cleared, she began on the shelf at the top of the wardrobe. Old, worn handbags were taken down, checked for content and bagged. Two expensive hats, in dusty plastic bags -when had they been worn? - were put in the Vincent de Paul box. Then she felt something at the back. She dragged it forward until she could get a grip on it and lift it out. It was a shoebox. It was light but there was definitely something in it. She pulled over the bedroom chair, sat on it and placed the shoebox in front of her on the bed.

The box was covered in dust. It had not been touched for many years. What was in it? Something that had belonged to her father, retained for sentimental reasons, eventually forgotten? Unlikely. Her mother was not a sentimental person. She could not afford to be. Papers to do with the house, something like that? More likely.

Hannah removed the lid. Yes, that is what it contained, papers that had been important once upon a time, receipts, quotations for work on the house, double glazing, the kitchen extension, the refitting of the bathroom, the attic insulation, and correspondence about the work. Each project's papers were neatly held together by paper clips. As Hannah lifted each out in turn and examined it, she recalled the work and the excitement at the time of getting those significant improvements done. It was all so long ago, historical papers now, one could say.

When she picked up the last sheaf of papers, she saw beneath it three envelopes addressed to her and recognised immediately Tom Byrne's large, clear, almost childish, handwriting. Her heart stopped, then beat harder. The envelopes were blue, one open, two unopened. Her hands began to shake. The sheaf of papers dropped to the floor. She picked up the open envelope.

Everything happened in slow motion. She could hardly breathe. She removed the letter. "Dear Hannah, I miss you every hour of every day." She read the letter slowly, with tears in her eyes, her heart racing. She read it filled with the emotion and excitement she would have felt if she had received it when it had been written.

Tom told her that he had a job and had started studying at

night. He wanted her to come to London, where he was sure she would get work immediately. If she couldn't come, he would return to Dublin as soon as he had completed his studies. "Thinking of you all the time, All my love always, Tom."

She finished the letter, her shoulders shaking with sobs, tears running down her cheeks. She leaned forward, her elbows on her knees, her face in her hands, the letter against her cheek, wet with tears. Although her heart had broken all those years ago, when she had not heard from Tom, and although she had felt the wound many times since, she had never cried, until now. Now, she cried uncontrollably until exhausted.

When she stopped crying, she sat motionless, the letter still in her hand, staring blindly out the bedroom window. She sat like that for what seemed a long time. She heard the distant sound of traffic. A dog barked. The window brightened with sunshine and darkened again. Somebody banged a car door. A car engine started and faded away.

When life returned, she put the letter back in its envelope, removed the two unopened envelopes from the shoebox, and held the three gently to her breast for a moment. She took the three letters downstairs to the living room fireplace. Her mother never smoked but she kept matches in the fuel box beside the fireplace.

Hannah found them, as she had expected. In the fuel box, there were old newspapers for fire-lighting. Hannah crumpled a few pages into loose balls and put them in the grate. She placed the three envelopes side-by-side, one opened, two unopened, on top of the newspaper and lit the fire. The letters smouldered at first and then burst into brilliant flame.

Beginners Short Story Winner

"Hello Again"

By Jacinta Lowndes,
Portrane, co. Dublin

A mother remembers the heartbreaking decision of her youth, the trip on the bus with her new-born baby all those years ago ...

I AM HERE AGAIN. The smell is the same. The wooden floor has seen a hundred years of polish and thousands of footsteps. The fireplace in the corner lies vacant and dusty. I sit still trying to listen to sounds in the building. All I can hear is my heart thumping so fast I think it will explode through my chest. I notice my fingers picking invisible pieces of fluff off my dress. A habit I picked up all those years ago.

The mind is funny. It plays tricks, blocks memories, filters, tints recollections, I suppose it's to protect you so you don't go mad, perhaps you'll see the past as not so bad. But as I sit here in this empty room waiting, my mind finally allows in that day. Each detail comes rushing in. I feel goose bumps as I suddenly remember everything about him.

The 46A bus had left O'Connell Street and crawled through the Christmas traffic and slush. A mix of hail and sleet seemed to come straight down from heaven and I was so glad to get on the bus. I made a bee line for the back seat hoping the heat from the engines would keep us warm, the exact change ready in my handfor the conductor so I wouldn't have to disturb the baby in my arms.

The child mesmerised me. I could barely take my eyes off him. It was like falling in love again. I thought his eyes were the biggest, bluest eyes I had ever seen. When he blinked, his long eyelashes fluttered gently open and close. Every part of him was perfect. I swear I thought angels had created him.

I remember the freezing winds seemed to enter the bus with every passenger that got on. Each time the doors opened the gale came in, whoosh, like a ghost trying to find a bare piece of skin to enter into your bones. That ghost wouldn't get to him, I had him in his best outfit and wrapped in the warmest white blanket. I remember the tiny pieces of fluff the wool left on my good coat.

My Ma had bought me that coat when I came to Dublin first – that had been two years prior. "You can show them how to dress properly, mind though it's for Mass and weekends, not for parading up and down Grafton Street on any evening."

She had winked at me the way she did when she meant it, but knew I would do my own thing. God, how I missed her.

The last time I wore the coat was standing at her graveside. I had sat beside her hospital bed and held her hand as she passed, the pain leaving her body, as peace descended on her. I held her soft hands until the cold seeped into them. I remember rubbing them to keep the blood flowing. To pretend she hadn't left me. What would she say now?

The Christmas lights twinkled as the bus travelled down Dawson Street and I closed my eyes to blind myself from the celebration – I still do it on the bus – close my eyes and the lights flash in your eyelids creating patterns and memories. All I see now are memories of that day.

An elderly woman sat beside me. She was one of those women who chatted to everyone and expected your life story in return. Of course the thing about travelling with a baby is that they attract the kindness of strangers and when the conductor shouted "Fares please", she dismissed him with a wave of her bus pass and a harsh "Shush, baby's asleep," and she turned to chat to me.

"You'd want to keep that little mite well wrapped up."

I nodded and turned back to the window. I held the baby tightly. His little face wriggled with the movement, blinking open his eyes to see what was happening. His lips parted as if expecting my breast.

"Is it a boy or girl?"

"A boy."

"Ahh, boys are easier to rear you know. How old?"

"Eleven days."

"God, aren't you great to be out and about. The shops are packed aren't they? Were you Christmas shopping?"

"No, no."

"That's a beautiful blanket, did you crochet it yourself?"

I gave in. I told her I did. It only took me a few days. I had bought the wool in Clery's especially. I remember she felt it and examined the needle work saying it was gorgeous and soft.

"Soft as a baby's bum" she said and we both laughed.

"Are you going somewhere nice?" – she gently enquired.

"Ah no, I was having him baptised in Clarendon Street."

"Oh, good girl. What name did you give him?"

"Michael Henry, after his Da."

"That's a strong name. Well Michael Henry," she said as she poked an arthritic finger into the blanket, "I wish you health and happiness, may God bless you, you're a beauty alright."

Michael opened his eyes and smiled – he lit up the world with that gummy smile. It melted your heart and it made us smile and coo at him.

"And is Dad not with you, is he at work?"

"Oh he is, yeh. He's in England, in Liverpool," I fidgeted with the wedding ring on my finger, another piece of my mother.

"Sure he's the image of his Da, he has his eyes, his lips, the fair hair, sure there's not a bit of me in him." I laughed.

I reached inside the blanket to check he was warm enough, and his fingers clung around mine.

"Even his hands - hasn't he fine hands?" I said showing them.

The old woman stroked them and Michael's fingers curled around hers.

"God, they are fine working hands alright, sure any grown man would be proud of them." She said nudging me.

I kissed them gently and placed them back into the warmth of the blanket.

"Oh they will work alright. He'll teach or play music. They won't dig roads or plough fields. No. Michael will be different.

He will finish his schooling. I will see to that, he will get the chance to be someone." I half whispered this to the child, as if I had the power to promise him everything.

The old woman scolded me, like I was her own, told me not to be thinking above my station. "Hard work never killed anyone." she advised.

I conceded to her that I just wanted the best for him.

"Ah and why wouldn't you? You're a good mother and don't let anyone tell you otherwise."

At Stillorgan I rang the bell, I was glad to leave the conversation behind, despite the fact that the hail and sleet pelted down against me as I got off the bus. I almost smothered the child against my coat trying to protect him.

I remember waiting for the pedestrian lights to change so I could cross the road to the main gates of the house. The avenue up to it seemed endless and yet not long enough. The gardens on either side perfectly kept with patches of snow here and there.

The grey house was huge, with three stories of windows, the smallest at the top. The front door was glossy black with a big shiny brass knocker. I lifted it and gently tapped on the door hoping no one would answer but the sound echoed in the hallway beyond. Michael began to stir and cry looking for his food. The door opened.

"Good evening. Come in child."

I remember being thankful to step in out of the biting cold, yet the hall felt colder and I stood there shivering. It smelled like a mixture of my old primary school and a funeral mass. I noticed a statue of Our Lady holding baby Jesus and smiled at her in recognition of her love for her son. I thought, "We have a lot in common Mary."

The front door closed and I turned to find the nuns arms outstretched, awaiting delivery of my precious child.

It was then I knew. It was then I felt the love that all mothers feel. Regardless of how the child comes into the world, regardless of sin or sinner, the feeling that you would do anything for this innocent bundle is overwhelming. You would love them, protect them, do what's best for them, anything. I had believed I was doing all those things by handing him up. I was told that was what I was doing. "A scorned woman", my father had shouted at me, "A disgrace with no choice, no money, no husband."

She smiled at me the way some nuns do –that gentle, condescending way.

"It's best you give him to me."

Best for who? I thought as she took him. I fixed his blanket for the last time. "Please take care of him, he's due his feed."

As if sensing my emotion Michael cried a piercing wailing cry. The nun tightened her hold. "I'll see he goes to a good respectable home. You go on your way child and may God forgive you."

Those words haunted me. I try to shake them from my head. I hear voices outside, a knock on the door downstairs brings me back to the present and I glance around what would have been a nun's bedroom and is now a waiting room for people like me. The crucifix on the wall is the only decoration. I wonder did he ever sleep here. Was he here the first night I left him? While I stood outside empty – handed, realisation dawning, banging on the door until my hands ached, begging for him back.

I understood then what a broken heart was, that it could actually break and yet keep beating. All I was left with were the white pieces of blanket fluff which had clung to my coat.

The elderly woman's words "You're a good mother," went round my head that first night. I was. I returned to the convent every day for weeks looking for him. Telling the nuns I wanted him back, always told to go home, to forget, to pray. Eventually they told me the baby wasn't there, he was gone to a decent family.

So I resorted to waiting, knowing I would eventually see my son again. Last September the phone call came. My son wished to meet me. He had found me, through a mountain of paperwork and years of reconciliation in his own mind. I spoke to God for the first time in twenty seven years and thanked him.

We wrote to each other initially. To introduce ourselves, give a snapshot of our lives. I told him I was married with three other sons. I was a florist, I hated ironing, loved the X factor and football. He was married with a daughter, worked as a teacher, hated ironing and loved football. I was so proud.

A tap on the door. I stand up, my stomach somersaults. Breathe. I walk towards the opening door. I stare at the stranger walking in; trying to take him in. Trying to see is he pleased, sad or angry to see me. I try to recognise the eleven day old baby I gave away. He is gone. My beautiful baby has grown into a tall handsome man with beautiful eyes and a kind face, the image of his father.

I hold out my trembling hand to shake his.

"I'm Sheila, your Mother."

But Michael pushes my hand away. Instead he pulls me into his chest and holds me just like I held him all those years before. Like only a mother and son can hold each other. He whispers, "Hello again Mam."

I can't believe it. I'm afraid to let him go. Twenty seven years of waiting, of trying to sleep with a broken heart. I don't want to lose him again. I feel tears begin to flow as he sits me down.

IN HOT PURSUIT ...

By Colette Murphy,
Wicklow

The Jacobs Biscuits advertising campaign, featuring Jim Figgerty and the secret of getting the figs into the fig rolls, was one of the talking points of the 1960s

THE SECRET of how Jacob's got the figs into fig rolls was a closely guarded one in the Sixties with only one man privy to the information. So when he went missing from his workplace in March 1969, the management of Jacob's Biscuit factory had a huge problem on their hands. They feared the worst. What if he sold the secret to their competitors? The whole future of the fig-roll was in jeopardy.

They immediately informed the public to be on the look out for the errant Jim Figgerty. Large posters of the "Fig Meister" himself began to appear on billboards all over the country with huge slogans asking the public "Have you seen this man?" or messages addressed to the fugitive such as "Jim Figgerty, please call your office."

Wearing a stone-coloured mackintosh and a trilby hat, and sporting a large handlebar moustache, Jim Figgerty had all the appearances of a wanted man. And so it came to pass that two months after he went missing, I unwittingly became involved in the case of the missing Jim Figgerty.

I was on my way home from work travelling by bus from Dublin city centre to my bed-sit in Rathgar. The bus was overcrowded as usual with many passengers standing in the aisle. Squashed onto one of the television seats at the back of the vehicle, I was looking forward to my evening meal of Vesta Beef Curry. I was completely oblivious to everything around me as the bus stopped and started letting people on and off.

Suddenly I heard a young girl scream out excitedly "It's him! It's him!" I was immediately awoken from my reverie. Without warning she jumped up from her backward-facing seat at the front of the bus, pushed her way through the crowd towards the back screaming excitedly "Stop the bus! Stop the bus! Jim Figgerty has just got off! Come on before he gets away!" she said gesturing to the passengers to come with her.

Immediately everyone got caught up in the excitement. She had a blond beehive hairstyle, miniskirt and stiletto heels, and many of the passengers including myself jumped up and followed her onto the platform. Amused at the situation, the bus conductor obligingly rang the bell twice bringing the bus to an abrupt halt.

As we jumped off the bus we could see Jim Figgerty wearing his trademark clothes walking at a steady pace ahead of us. "Come on, hurry up or he'll get away," shouted Blondie as a group of us, mainly married women and young girls, sprinted in hot pursuit of the fugitive.

With calls of "Jim Figgerty we see you!" and "Wait for us Jim!" the fugitive suddenly looked back, his large handlebar moustache very much in evidence, to see a crowd like baying hounds running after him. With a shocked look on his face he began to run, dodging down leafy lanes, across a park and into quiet residential streets. The faster he ran the faster we did laughing and calling out to him along the way.

Moving like a greyhound, Jim turned down a narrow road and disappeared into a house on the left. Just as we reached the wrought-iron gate the door closed behind him. With chants of "We want Jim Figgerty!" and "Come out Jim Figgerty!" the neighbours came out to see what all the commotion was about. They seemed highly amused at the situation, gathering in groups laughing.

Like a falling star, one of them suddenly broke away and moved in our direction. "That's not Jim Figgerty" she told us laughing heartily, "That's Mr. Boyle. He works in the Civil Service". We suspected she was trying to put us off the scent and refused to listen to her. After all we had seen him for ourselves.

Some minutes later the door of the fugitive's house opened and a pale nervous-looking woman came out. "Please go away" she pleaded. "My husband is not Jim Figgerty".

"Yes he is!" said Blondie. "We SAW him go into your house!"

"But he's not Jim Figgerty" she protested. "Please go home and leave us alone".

A half hour later, with no sign of Jim coming out of the house, I decided it was time to leave as my stomach was grumbling and I needed to get ready for my evening out with friends.

The following day I turned on the radio to hear the usual daily bulletin on Jim's whereabouts the previous day. As I listened excitedly expecting to hear the outcome of the previous evening, I was shocked to hear the announcer say: "Jim Figgerty was correctly spotted in Howth yesterday evening at 5.00 p.m. by a man walking his dog".

I don't know who we followed that day but we must have put the fear of God in the poor man!

THE PAIN OF LEAVING

BY MARION RILEY,
Prestwich, Manchester

It's the late 1950s in Ireland and twelve years old Carmel tells us what it is like when her father has to close his shop and the family has to emigrate

MY NAME IS CARMEL, I'm twelve years of age and I'm lying on my bed from where, if I listen hard enough, I can hear my parents talking downstairs. It's May 1958 and they're saying they'll have to leave Ireland. I know that means emigration, which is not like going on a holiday, but being forced to leave forever.

Daddy can't find work anywhere. He says half the country lives on credit. That's why he's had to sell his grocery business. He's such a kind man that he let a lot of poor people have food from the shop without paying. He listened to their hard luck stories and they were unable to pay him back.

He says we might go to South Africa or Canada where my uncles live but he'salso considering a job in England from where he could come home to us every now and then.

I don't want my daddy to leave us but neither do I want to go anywhere, especially now when I've started a new school, made so many friends and due to make my Confirmation. I just want to stay here with the fields behind me, the open spaces and the freedom. I don't want to go to a foreign country. I want to spend my life here in this country, where I was born and which I love so much.

Please dear God, don't let us have to go. Please find work for Daddy. I promise I'll be good in the future. I'll help Mammy around the house and look after my baby brother and my

16

sisters. I'll help with the ironing and washing and making the beds. I'll do anything, even bake a rabbit pie though these poor creatures should be allowed to run around free, not eaten by hungry humans.

Mammy and Daddy have spent the last week talking about emigrating, but every time I come into the room, they shut up. They should at least include me in their conversation, give me a choice as to whether we go or stay, ask my advice. I know what I would tell them... emigration is the saddest word in anyone's language, it's to be avoided at all costs.

Not that they'd take any notice of me, I'm only a child. But I don't care, I'll just stay here with one of my friends. See if they like that.

June and it looks as if we're going to Canada where Uncle John lives. He left Ireland during the civil war, many, many years before I was born. He was only sixteen when he saw his father and brothershiding from the men who were once their friends. That is what civil war is, brother fighting brother, friend fighting friend.

Is this what they fought for, the freedom to emigrate?

My uncle made a home in a part of Canada where only red Indians lived. Now Canada could be very exciting. I've always fancied living in a tepee. In fact, I'd really like to be an Indian with their long black hair and brown skin but I don't think they live in tents any more.

The sun is shining today and I'm going to try to put the thought of leaving home out of my mind while I wander the fields with all the neighbours' dogs. I love these dogs, sometimes more than people. I don't need to speak for they know what I'm feeling.

There's Rory the Irish red setter who runs around as if there is no tomorrow. Then there's Freddy a fox terrier, always full of mischief; Shep, the sheepdog, who chases anything that moves and, of course, my own fluffy, white dog called Beloney who looks at me with such love in his eyes. If he were a cat he'd purr.

How I love the countryside, the speckled horses belonging to the gypsies, the blackberry and hawthorn bushes, the mountains,the secret hiding and climbing places.

JULY and Daddy's gone alone to Manchester. He's got a job as a shop assistant. That must be strange for him after having his own shop. We all can't stop crying. It's the saddest day of our lives. We've got no father at home now, like so many of my friends.

AUGUST and it's Mammy's birthday. For four weeks now I've had the big bed and Mammy all to myself. It's brilliant and sometimes I forget all about my father. But how I wish she wouldn't cry so much after speaking to Daddy from the 'phone box half a mile away. Every fortnight she cycles there and comes back in a right state.

She says she's lonely but she's got me and my sisters and brother. My sisters envy me sleeping in her bed, but I'm the oldest in the family and I have to take care of her now. She's no longer the happy, cheerful mother I used to know. I keep finding her crying. I'm so worried. Please don't let her even think of following Daddy to Manchester.

SEPTEMBER and in a couple of days Daddy 's coming home to spend a weekend with us. Mammy is so happy. She's a different person. She's treated herself to the hairdressers and even though money is so very short, she bought material to make herself a new frock. It's pink gingham and she wears it with a white flouncy underskirt. She looks lovely and says she'll make my sisters and I some skirts with the material that's left.

I'll feel very shy when I see Daddy again, it's been such long time since he held me in his arms.

Daddy's been here a few days now and he keeps saying how much he misses Mammy and us. He worries about her feeling lonely but she's not alone, she's got us for company. He wants us all to go to Manchester. He says there are picture houses and big shops with escalators and a lot of schools to choose from. I don't want to go to a mixed school with English boys. All I want is to stay here, learn Irish and attend the girls only convent school.

OCTOBER and I feel really fed up. Even though I've prayed to every saint I've ever heard of, no miracle has happened to stop us emigrating. We're still going. Mammy had a word with the nuns at school because of all my praying. I think she thought I was becoming a saint. The Reverend mother said the right road to being a saint was to accept the will of God and to obey your parents.

NOVEMBER and we're leaving in a month's time, I'll never spend another Christmas here. I don't want to go to England. Don't want to go where people are not friendly, where the men wear bowler hats and carry umbrellas. I've been told that they even wheel prams and that the women go out to work, instead of staying at home and looking after their children.

I hope Mammy isn't thinking of going to work, I'd die of shame. She said that a lot of women work in factories and wear clogs for shoes. I hope God spares her from this fate. Her bunions would get worse.

DECEMBER 8th, 1958: we are leaving and Beloney, my little fluffy dog whom I love so much, has been taken away forever by the next door neighbours. He's sitting on their windowsill whining and barking.

All my friends and relatives have come and gone from miles around to say their goodbyes. My twelve aunts and uncles and about thirty cousins held on to me in tears. My school friends brought me presents and some of them said that I could stay in their houses but I couldn't leave my family to emigrate without me.

The green hills and purple mountains are especially beautiful today. The horses in the fields behind the houses are even more playful than usual. They don't know of my pain. We are really leaving. I'll never see my dog again. Everything is changed, nothing will ever be the same. I say goodbye to my happy childhood, goodbye to the child that once was me.

I'm crying inside as the boat leaves Dun Laoghaire. No tears run down my face like my mothers, but I can hardly breathe with the pain of my feelings. My baby brother is crying non-stop but my sisters are really excited. They don't understand that we are emigrating. To them it's an exciting adventure. Some of my cousins have come to the port and as the boat leaves, they run down the pier waving and shouting at us. I feel as if my heart will break especially when the horn blows. It's the most lonesome sound I've ever heard, like a lament I'd imagine the banshee would make.

We stay on deck watching the shores of Ireland disappear and then go inside to eat our jam sandwiches. The sea is quite rough, people are slipping and sliding on spilled drink and food and there's a lot of vomit in the toilets. We arrive in Holyhead and then have to wait a few hours for the train to Manchester.

On the train I fall asleep and dream I'm back in Ireland making giant haystacks, picking pink mushrooms from under cows' dung and tasting the juice of freshly picked blackberries. I float through clouds and gaze down on green fields that look like patchwork quilts and white thatched cottages. I wake up with a snort and am most embarrassed to find my head resting on the shoulder of a young man who helped us with our suitcases.

Daddy is waiting for us at the train station. I can't resist his outstretched arms nor the look of sadness in his eyes. It's not his fault, he did his best but why did he bring us here.

Manchester seems so cold and industrial. My heart turns over at the old house that Daddy has chosen for us to live in. There is a factory chimney behind the back yard. But at least we have our own place to live in. I see notices outside boarding houses saying No Blacks, No Irish, No Dogs, so we would not be welcome in these places but I don't know why.

I can't understand what the people are saying. They drop their aitches and add them on where they aren't supposed to be. They say Ter Ra for goodbye and something else that sounds like Ta Ta. They call me luv and every time I hear this word, it makes me smile.

The house is cold and damp and the area is all built up. The very air is different with a strong smell of fish and chips. There are no fields around. Mammy hides her disappointment and talks about taking in boarders. I hope she puts up a sign saying Irish and Blacks welcome. I don't think it would be a good idea to have dogs, much and all as I would love them.

We need furniture for we have nothing, no beds, tables or chairs. It's very cold and the floor is so hard to sleep on.

NEW YAR'S EVE and we all stay up to see 1959 in. We now have beds, a table and chairs and even a second hand piano. We dance jigs and Daddy sings I'll Take You Home Again Kathleen to Mammy, whose eyes fill up with tears.

I constantly ask my parents when were we going back. They always say in a year or two, just like the other Irish people they've met. They all think there'll be more jobs in the Sixties and a welcome back to the land of our birth.

I live in hope that they are right. I desperately need to believe them. Please God, tomorrow, when the time is ripe, let us all go home.

MEMORIES OF POP

BY PAULA REDMOND,
Gorey, Co. Wexford

In my mind I can still walk into his house. I can see the calendar from 1987 that was always on the wall, the old dial telephone and his mandolin in the corner.

MY GRANDFATHER, Pop as we knew him, was one of the last of his generation when he passed on aged ninety. He was born in 1910 and was able to recall events to me that I only knew from the pages of history. He remembered the Black and Tans marching the streets and he knew people who had succumbed to the tuberculosis outbreak.

He worked in England during World War 2, making the long journey to Belfast with his "attaché case" as he called it to get the boat to Stranraer. My grandmother would post woodbine cigarettes to him hidden in newspapers to stop customs confiscating them.

His house in Arklow, Co. Wicklow was steeped in family and maritime history. My great-grandmother, Kate Tyrrell, a lady mariner of the 1800's, had bought the house, my grandmother was born there and my mother's family raised in it.

Like other houses in this maritime town, its intrinsic link with the sea was visible from various objects dotted around - the old sailors chest in the front room, the oil lamps from the family ship. My grandmother died before I was born but her presence could still be felt.

Her piano, un-played, sat in the front room. As children we would bang on it thinking we could miraculously teach ourselves how to play but all we did was make a racket and put it out of tune. Her Leaving Certificate hanging on the wall amazed me as it was completed under British rule.

The sailor's chest was filled to the brim with her sheet music; songs from musicals, classical pieces and even Beatles tunes. As a child I pondered at the strange symbols written in the corners, 5d etc. When my aunt referred to this as "back when we used the old LSD", I was shocked to think she had taken drugs back in the swinging sixties! Decimal currency had come in long before I was born!

Like in all Irish houses, the kettle was always on the boil. Pop had an old style range that always seemed to give him trouble. Often we would come in to find him on his hands and knees stoking it, the air heavy with soot and smoke.

I would be sent over the hill to the bakery a few doors down to get melt-in-the-mouth doughnuts, fat with cream and jam, or warm hot cross buns at Easter. We didn't seem to worry about weight, though Pop's Jack Russell Daisy should have been a warning to us. Her paws could barely be seen peeping out under her belly due to all the biscuits and cakes Pop fed her.

Pop always chose to spend Christmas Day alone. He wasn't bothered about Christmas and insisted on getting a cooked chicken for dinner. On many occasions my mother attempted to put up some decorations despite his protestations. I would fetch his fairly ragged artificial tree from the top of the wardrobe, blow the dust off and turn down the branches that had seen better days.

On St. Stephen's day he would come to our house armed with his accordion or "box" as he called it and mandolin. He was a drummer in his younger days. He recalled the many dance halls he had played in and the innocence of those times. He had travelled to villages such as Avoca and laughed about how even though he was only a few miles from home,he thought he was at the other side of the country!

His mother used to starch his brilliant white shirt for gigs and he recalled how the women all chased him! My grandmother was a pianist and accordion player and had a band. She and my grandfather met when she hired him to play with her. He kept his drum kit under his bed until the day he died.

With his well-pawed songbooks, he played and laughed and drank more than one whiskey. One of his favourites "I'll Tell Me Ma" got many replays. It was after one of these sessions that he headed off on the bus home.

A few hours later our phone rang and a man at the other end asked, "Is this the family of a Mr. Pat Mahon?" I thought he must have died on the bus! He had fallen asleep and ended up in Busaras in Dublin. I travelled with my father to collect him and can still see his figure with his grey overcoat and hat standing embarrassed at the bus stop!

I forget sometimes that he is gone. I find myself using his sayings like "they'd live on the clippings of tin" to describe meanness. In my mind I can still walk into his house. I can see the calendar from 1987 that was always on the wall, the old dial telephone and his mandolin in the corner.

Most of all I remember the happiness and the laughter.

SILLY OUL FOOL

BY BEN RITCHIE,
Downpatrick, Co. Down

*Patsy is persuaded by his granddaughter to buy some hens and
a rooster at a car boot sale, but he had reckoned without his
neighbour's rooster paying a courtesy call*

PATSY LEANT over the gate looking down the wee field.
It wasn't really a field, more of a large garden with some
ancient fruit trees at the end furthest from the house.
Patsy's father had told him once that they had been planted
as a wind break years ago by his grandfather. They'd likely be
standing long after Patsy was gone.

Today Patsy wasn't pondering his own mortality. Instead he
was admiring the new rooster he had bought the night before at
a car boot sale. He had only gone because his grand –daughter,
Molly, had wanted to go and look for some books. Molly's
mum and dad were working so Patsy had said he would take
her.

She had dragged him by the hand around the stalls, talking
and laughing all the time. She was a joy to be with and, if truth
be told, Patsy had been delighted at the opportunity to take
her. Molly was the apple of his eye.

They were on their way out of the car boot sale when Molly
spotted the wooden crate, tucked under a table, with half
a dozen hens and a rooster in it. The hens, of no particular
breed, were a rainbow of colours and stood quietly in awe of
their surroundings. Only the rooster gazed around and crowed
defiantly at the passers-by.

"The hens look so sad. Why don't you get them, Granda?"
said Molly.

"Now what do I need hens for, Molly dear?", replied Patsy. "Anyway, your Granny would go mad if I brought them home. And I've no-where to keep them."

"But Granda, you could put them in the wee field and keep them in that old shed beside the ash tree. Granny could use the eggs for baking. She's always saying that shop eggs aren't as good as your own. And later on you could have chicks. I love chicks, don't you?"

Patsy could feel himself weakening. Molly's mother, Caithlin, had always been able to get her own way with him and he could sense history repeating itself. It was time for diversionary tactics.

"Sure we'll go home and see what we'd need to keep some hens," said Patsy, " and then look out for some. What do you say?"

She didn't have to reply. He could see the disappointment in her face. She didn't make a scene or rhyme on, she just picked up her books and walked away. That was part of the reason Patsy loved her. With a heartfelt sigh he caught up with her.

"If I get the hens you'll have to do something for me."

"Oh Granda I'll do anything," said Molly, beaming with happiness as she threw her arms around him and kissed him on the cheek.

After some quick bargaining Patsy got the hens for twenty pounds. He even got the crate. Turns out the seller was getting rid of all his birds and was happy to get rid of this last lot. On the way home in the van Molly repeated how great it would be for everyone to have the hens.

She would collect the eggs when she was staying and maybe when there were chicks she would bring some of them to school to show her friends. As they pulled into the yard Molly turned to Patsy and asked, seriously:

"What is it you want me to do for you, Granda, for getting the hens?"

Patsy turned to her with a serious face and said quietly: "I want you to do something very brave, something that I can't do. And you'll have to do it alone."

Molly felt a little uneasy. Her Granda was never like this. "What?", she whispered.

"I want you to go into your Granny Kate and tell her we have six hens and a rooster."

For a moment Molly was unsure what to do. Then she saw her Granda start to grin and she started to smile.

"Oh Granda," was all she said. Then she jumped out of the van and ran, laughing, into the house. Patsy didn't know what Molly said but when he went into the kitchen he was greeted by a wink from a smiling Molly, and "You silly oul fool," from his wife.

So that's how he found himself leaning over the gate that morning. The hens were sticking together as they fed, moving around cautiously. The rooster looked up and swaggered over to Patsy. He was tall, mostly white with a golden breast and black tips to his wings. He stretched himself to his full height and crowed challengingly.

Almost immediately a response arrived on the soft breeze. Patsy's rooster instinctively responded. That was Tony's rooster up on the next farm. Patsy went about his work, leaving the two roosters to challenge and counter challenge. Patsy went down to feed the hens at about four o'clock. Kate had given him a few kitchen scraps and he had some meal in a bucket. He was feeling quite pleased with the way things had turned out. Molly was happy, and Kate, had come round to the idea of having hens far more easily than he had expected. Yes, life was good.

The first thing he noticed was the hens pecking, nervously, around a ball of feathers down by the gooseberry bush. Patsy rushed over, tripping over a stone hidden by the tall grass. He stumbled to a halt, breathing heavily.

The head was a swollen bloody mess. The feathers were blood stained and in places on the breast, pale, torn skin could be seen. The once tall tail feathers lay limp and matted with blood. How was he going to tell Molly?

After he had shooed the hens away with his cap Patsy realised that the wings of this rooster were black, completely black. At the same moment Molly's rooster came out from behind the bush and crowed victoriously. He'd lost a few feathers and had a few bloody patches but there didn't seem to be any serious injuries.

Suddenly Patsy realised what had happened. Tony's rooster had come down over the fields to see off the newcomer but had met his match. For a moment Patsy felt a sense of pride in the rooster, until he heard a jeep slowing to come up the lane. Tony! He came every Friday afternoon. His excuse was to deliver the local paper but Patsy knew that it was Kate's tea and scones he was really after.

Tony had often boasted about what a great rooster he owned. Reared from a chick, it was as black as night, with a temper to match. Tony had called it The Devil. Even the dogs were scared of it. What would he say when he found out that his pride and joy had been killed by a blow-in.

Patsy grabbed Molly's rooster and threw him into the shed with a handful of meal to keep him quiet. As he barred the door he heard the jeep's engine die and Tony's quick footsteps echoing on the concrete yard. Something was wrong. Tony usually went straight into the house for his tea. Patsy felt a lead weight in his belly. Somehow Tony knew. Patsy managed to throw an old sack over the body just before Tony strode into the wee field.

"Tony," started Patsy.

"Ah no, no, no" moaned Tony. " I should've known." Patsy had failed to cover the whole body and the bloodied head lay exposed like some swollen boil. Tony pulled off his cap and slapped his leg with it.

"Now Tony, let me explain," said Patsy. They'd been friends for years.

"What's there to explain Patsy?" replied Tony. "It's plain what happened here. The Devil didn't like the idea of another rooster in his territory so he came down over the Long Field and killed your boy. What a mess!"

Patsy was stunned. Tony obviously thought that the dead bird was not his. Should he play along or tell the truth. Tony must have taken Patsy's silence for grief or anger. "Now Patsy, you know what The Devil's like, he's as wicked as can be. Your boy didn't stand a chance against a champion like him."

As Patsy listened to Tony rambling on about the extraordinary powers of The Devil, he was amazed by this man's belief in the superiority of his rooster. The very same rooster that was stiffening as rigor mortis set in. The decider was when Tony said, "You know Patsy you should have known better than bring a rooster round here with The Devil just over the hedge."

"You're right Tony," said Patsy, with a sigh of resignation. "The Devil rules this land. What was I thinking about? I'm going to bury this boy where he fell and plant a bush over him. But where is the black boy?"

"I'd say he's back home, full of himself," said Tony with a hint of smugness. "I'll go on up and see. Are you all right ,Patsy?

"Aye. Sure this boy was nothing to me."

"No hard feelings, Patsy. I don't want us to fall out over this," said Tony sincerely.

Patsy felt a little guilty, but not enough. "If we didn't fall out forty years ago when Kate married me and not you, we're not going to fall out over some puffed-up rooster."

"You can't have all the luck Patsy. Tell Kate sorry, but I'll have to go and see to The Devil. He might have a scratch or two. There'll be no living with him now." Tony strode away, turning back to wave before he got in into his jeep. Moments later he was leaving a trail of dust as he tore down the lane.

Patsy stood looking at what was left of The Devil. "I don't think Tony'll find you up in the yard, boy," said Tony. He opened up the bag and lifting the dead bird by the legs he put the body in. The hens by now had lost interest and were moving over towards the shed, from where muffled crows could be heard. Patsy went over and pulled open the old door. The rooster marched out over to the hens and started to scrape in a patch of loose soil as if nothing had happened.

"What was wrong with Tony?"

He jumped at the sound of Kate's voice.

"He went out of here like the devil himself was after him," she continued.

Patsy laughed and walked over to Kate smiling: "Looking for

The Devil, more like."

Kate stared at him: "What have you done, you oul eegit?"

Patsy put his arm round Kate and told her the story as they walked up the yard to the back door. She stopped when Patsy told her how Tony had boasted about The Devil's superiority.

"Tony always had an air about himself," said Kate. "That's why he assumed that was our rooster. The silly oul fool." They smiled at each other as only a loving husband and wife can, and walked arm in arm in for their tea.

MATCH MAKING

BY MARTIN MALONE,
Athy, Co. Kildare

Middle-aged bachelors Art and Liam have been trying for years to meet up with 'the right woman' without much success, and now they decide to get in contact with a match maker in county Kerry ...

" LONELINESS IS a torturer," Art said to him in the pub, going on, "it does bite at my joints and paints my heart black."

"Sure," Liam said, settling onto the bar stool at the counter, looking sidelong at his friend. "You don't have to paint me a picture. And you shouldn't go on so – we've tried but failed to find a cure. But-"

Art cut in, "We should do something about it."

He was a Murphy from Rathbridge, a man with land and no direct heir. A belly of a fellow with three chins you could use as steps, a nose you could shade under, and a mouth with teeth that he was in a habit of taking out.

Liam Flynn considered this at length. He had been a slow man all his life, deliberate. Some would say indecisive. His skin was drawn thinly over bones that a hungry dog of breeding would turn its behind to. He was a man who shared: Art was not.

"Any ideas as to what more we can do?" Liam said, his furry eyebrows colliding. He had not forgotten the disaster at Knock, where they'd been introduced to two fine widows, sisters. Art hadn't forgotten either and thought:

Oh that pair had thoughts to persuade us into selling our farms and big plans to buy villas in Spain. Villas on a golf course, no less. Lady golfers, indeed. Out pucking balls all day and we boys would have been left at home to do what?

Art said, "There's a fella in Dingle. I got to hear of him from Charlie Waters."

Charlie had married a Filipino woman much younger than himself; a gorgeous woman, well-mannered and full of gratitude at the least bit of kindness shown to her. He'd suggested to the boys that they follow the same path. And they'd considered this for a spell.

In the beginning Mary Lee had put a bit of spark in Charlie's eyes and a bounce to his step. But two years on he looked like a trod upon thistle. His two infants had blessed him with the look of the terrorised. What man in his 50's wanted to spend his days chasing after the needs of small children? Not Art. Kids, he knew, meant a serious outflow of cash and time.

"Who is he?" Liam said, ordering the same again from the barman with his forefinger.

"Denny Farrell."

"Denny," Liam mused, eyes on the ceiling where an old bicycle hung from; he used to know the old woman who owned it. "Farrell. Can't say the name has ever crossed my ears."

"I heard he hitched up 20 couples last year and there's not a sad soul in the forty of them. The man has been on the TV and all."

Art frowned, his thoughts on Lisdoonvarna five years ago: they'd hit it off with two lovely women from Kildare town at a dance. Oh great craic. But the boys had never seen a pair to guzzle as much alcohol and still remain standing and perfectly sober. Dublin women they were, originally, with high expectations.

Funny, too. "What's a farm?" one said, following up with a bout of screeching laughter that made people look their way. When the other said she had a beautiful wig for Liam, the boys gave each other the long look, their signal that it was time to exit. They consoled themselves later that the women hadn't got the legs for the wellingtons.

Liam said, "Are you listening to me at all?"

"I was thinking. What were you saying?"

"There might be hope for us – I was saying we shouldn't give up – and anyhow what were you thinking about?"

"Our successes in the past, Liam boy, what else?"

"Don't be sarcastic, Art. No woman wants to listen to sarcasm. It's not funny. They want a laugh. We mightn't be good to look at – but be japers we can make the women laugh."

"They've only to look at us."

Liam sighed. He was five years older than Art and believed he felt the pinch of loneliness more acutely. He looked younger than his friend – everyone said so, but still the oul cert didn't tell a lie. He said, "Wouldn't it be nice to have company in the winter evenings?"

They each lived down dark roads well beyond the reach of town lights, where the black of night had a weight.

Art said, "Aren't you gone all decisive of a sudden?"

Liam said, "I'm further down the road age-wise than you. I have to get a move on."

"Still," Art said, "how many of the boys have we seen go down the aisle owning a farm and come up owning half a one?"

"We can't take it with us – all we get is six feet in the end and I'm tired of being unlucky in love. Fed up, Art, with sitting in on winter nights with only the telly for company – you know..."

"Don't tell me."

"Lads our age-"

"I said don't tell me. I get fierce depressed when I hear of people I know who have died.I do be meeting meself coming out of the cemetery."

"See, that's what I'm saying. Art, let's go see what your Denny boy can do for us."

Art brought his pint to his lips and shrugged his shoulders lightly, "Fine, so."

Then he drummed his fingers on the table and stopped abruptly, "Do you know what I'm after thinking?"

"No. I'm not a mind reader like you."

"That we can change things about, do you follow?"

"Art?"

"Listen. We've put ourselves out there, right? Upfront boys

saying what we own, all that – we should say nothing – we should change our image."

"Go on."

"We should say we're on the dole – get into jeans and sprucy shirts, new hairstyles...for me anyway. Act modern. Act..."

Art looked again at the bike hanging from the ceiling and prayed for the wise old woman, Kitty the Hare, who used own it to give him some divine inspiration, "Act like we're not desperate. That's been our problem all along. We come across as desperate men, boys who'd settle for any woman as long as she'd have us."

"Aren't we though?"

"Yes. That's why we have to change our image."

Liam said quietly, "We'll put that idea to Denny."

Art, he knew, was always taking figaeries, lepping from one idea to the next like a child looting shelves at a sweet kiosk.

"We have to be frank with him, I suppose," Art admitted grudgingly.

"We do."

Art remained in the car while Liam went in to see the matchmaker. It rained hard. Denny lived in a whitewashed bungalow at the end of a tree -bordered boreen. A tall man with a smile that'd open your heart like it was a blossoming flower. A woman in her late 30's had answered the door to them, carrying a sleeping baby in her arms. Art and Denny had looked at each other and then Denny emerged with his smile and sent Art packing to the car. Not a really hospitable act, but Art was relieved as he was awkward around strangers and often his awkwardness rubbed off on them.

Liam emerged and walked to the car, shoulders hunched. Art wasn't sure if this was because of the rain or the burden of disappointment. And he hadn't time to ask as Denny was beckoning him with waves as large as a satellite dish.

Art said "Hello," to the woman as he walked through the sitting room into the kitchen. She smiled. He tried not to look at the mess: the baby clothes, Pampers, buggy...

In the kitchen, a large extension, a fire burned in a large green oval stove. Denny pointed to the table on which was a spread of notebooks, photographs, and documents.

"So," Denny said jovially, when they'd seated, "you're looking for a good woman?"

"I am."

"Hmm. Are you a man who likes to share?"

"Eh..."

"If you're not you're better off as you are."

"I-"

"Are you looking for love?"

"Yes."

"Okay – from the details you gave me over the phone, I've matched you with three women...I had another in mind but... anyway."

He passed photographs across the table. All of them pretty, if a little time-ravaged like him. Denny mentioned their names, their likes, dislikes. Art simply nodded. He wasn't drawn to the redhead, and the black haired woman had hard lips; while the third, though the least attractive of the trio and considerably overweight, he considered the best bet of a poor choice. Susan Daly, Denny said: "Separated, two children, eleven and twelve. A lovely family, into the country life, loves animals, and-"

"How old is she?"

"39."

"Too young."

"Divil a bit."

"I-"

"I had four photographs, but your friend picked the lady in the first photograph the moment he set eyes on her."

Art's curiosity showed on his face and Denny said, "I'll give you a look if you promise not to start fighting with him over her."

Denny smiled as Art gazed long and hard at the photograph. This woman was...shewas perfect, just his type. Short black hair, lovely lips, ice-blue eyes.

"Do you like children, Art?" Denny asked, pinching the

photograph from between Art's thumb and forefinger.

"I...no...no."

"That's my wife out there. She's 20 years younger than me and we're perfectly happy together and the child is a blessing at my age. I love them both very much."

"I wouldn't want the hassle of a young woman or childer. I wouldn't be able for it."

"Your heart's not the best?"

"Me heart's fine."

Denny said, "That's not the sort of heart I'm on about."

For part of the journey home, over the wind-swept Conor Pass, through a soaked Tralee, the men did not speak a word. Liam had sussed that Art was in foul humour by the strain in his features, the way his eyes looked way beyond the windscreen, the occasional mutter that was dark and tinged with underlying anger.

Finally, Liam said, "A nice man."

"Who?"

"Denny."

"Do you say?"

The uncomfortable silence in the car plummeted to a new depth.

Liam said, "Is something the matter?"

"Why would anything be the matter, all joking aside, why?"

"Did he not fix you up with a woman?"

Art said through clenched teeth, "Do I look like someone he found a match for?"

"Oh."

"You're sorted though."

"Yes, I'm looking forward to meeting up with Louise. I rang her. We had a great conversation when you were in with Denny – I was sort of hoping we'd have a double date, you know, to introduce us all to each other. And..." He saw Art's knuckles begin to turn white on the steering wheel and stopped talking.

Art sighed.

Liam said quietly, "Was there no one you liked?"

"A woman with kids he tried to pawn off on me. Who'd be wanting young pups wrecking his house and the peace in it?"

"Louise has a teenage daughter and a son."

"I hope you're not going to be a fool."

"How do you mean?"

"Just be careful."

Liam frowned so hard the pain cut along his forehead. He hadn't seen bitterness this sour in Art since the town lost the County Cup Final because of a refereeing error some years back. He supposed every man had things they simply couldn't take on the chin.

"I'll be very careful," Liam said.

"Why did you pick her?" Art said.

"I didn't – Denny did – he saw me put a note under the baby's pillow and..."

"You did what?"

"I put money – for luck – under the baby's pillow. It's a custom."

Art knew he would never have thought to do that if he lived to be a hundred, and saw what Denny meant when he asked if he was a man who liked to share. He was on his own.

Unless he changed. And change, he knew, wasn't in him.

PENNIES FROM HEAVEN

BY ANN ENGLISH,
Dun Laoghaire, Co. Dublin

I had my heart set on a red tartan bag I could see every day in McBirney's window, but the price was way beyond my means

AT THE BEGINNING of the year 2002, during the changeover from our decimal currency to the new Euro, we were encouraged to donate our left-over cash to a collection entitled 'Pennies from Heaven', from which a variety of charities would benefit. No doubt this title originated with the old song of the same name sung by Nat King Cole. However, I do firmly believe that it is possible that pennies can be sent from Heaven – if they are really, really badly needed.

When I left commercial college in June, 1952, and set forth to join the workforce at the age of seventeen, my first job was with C.I.E. in the Secretary's Office at Kingsbridge Station (now known as Hueston), where I was employed as a shorthand/typist. I earned the princely sum of £3. per week which I received in a sealed pay packet. This pay packet I duly handed over to my mother and she, in return, gave me my bus fare for the following week.

And that was it! There was no pocket money allowance. I had everything that I needed, the essentials that is. But for those little 'extras', the little treats that all girls love to be able to buy, there was no cash to spare. That's just the way it was in the early fifties. And there was no use in complaining, it just had to be accepted.

My journey to work necessitated hopping on two buses, the 7A which took me to city centre and then the No.78 to complete the trip. The terminus for the 78 bus was at McBirney's, a large

Department Store on Aston Quay. This was a store similar to Clerys and the premises have changed hands several times down through the years.

Each morning as I sat at the window of the bus awaiting its departure, I would gaze idly at the store window, feasting my eyes on the wonderful colourful display, just to pass the time. There was fashion and accessories, always an array of tempting gear to whet the appetite of any female. And then one morning I saw it – something I had been longing for for ages but could never afford to buy.

There it was sitting in the centre of the window. It was a red tartan bag, with a draw-string at the top and a strap to wear on the shoulder. **But,** it cost nine shillings and eleven pence, which I just did not have, nor would I ever have such an amount to 'squander' on non-essentials.

Well, morning after morning over the next couple of weeks I just sat gazing longingly at this bag – it was definitely calling me – I would even say taunting me, as though it knew its price was beyond my reach. On an occasional evening I would even cross the street on my return journey to have a closer look and to check if it had been sold! And yes, it was still there, exactly what I wanted, but would I ever be able to afford it?

And then it happened! My luck changed one wet, murky, sloppy evening, as I trudged my way up O'Connell Street to reach the 7A that left from Nelson's Pillar (before it was blown up!). Head bent against the wind, eyes cast down, I spotted it! A dirty, crumpled, soggy ten shilling note lay on the ground – certainly waiting for me.

I quickly pounced down and grabbed the note and held it so tightly in my clenched fist that I was afraid it would melt. Such a feeling of guilt swept over me! I expected a firm hand to land on my shoulder – the hand of the owner claiming it back. But that didn't happen – I couldn't believe my luck – this was just the amount I needed, with one penny to spare.

Well, needless to say, I doubled back to the store, oblivious of the rain, wind or the fact that I was missing my bus. I apologised to the shop assistant for the state of the note as

I tried to unravel it. Can you imagine my excitement? I had waited so long for this, it was unbelievable. I thought I'd never get home to show off my bit of style.

I slung the bag across my shoulder and proudly crossed the kitchen doing a 'modelling' act, when my mother remarked "I don't know what all the excitement is about, it's just like a horse's nose-bag." But I didn't care - her remark didn't spoil either the enjoyment of my purchase or my disbelief at how the money had come my way.

So that simple episode convinced me beyond all doubt, that one can be very lucky and pennies definitely can be sent from Heaven.

THE CATECHISM

By Patricia Foley,
Dunshaughlin, Co. Meath

*The fearsome Miss Griffin's catechism book has gone missing
and she initiates a search. She went down one row and emptied
everyone's belongings onto the floor*

" GET DOWN ON your knees and pray for the thief and
the liar among you". Like all the other pupils in third
class I did what Miss Griffin told us. As I said my prayers
I sneaked a look at the Teacher. Her face was purple and ugly
looking and the spit was running down her chin. As she worked
herself up into a frenzy, she sprayed spit all over those in the
front desks. Nobody attempted to wipe their faces. Although
we were only nine years old we knew that it wasn't wise to
catch her attention.

Miss Griffin was a religious fanatic. My Dad said it was
because she was from Kerry. He said they were all mad down
there. I don't know how he knew this because he had never
been to Kerry.

Every morning when we came into our bilious green
classroom, we said fiv e decades of the rosary. At twelve o'clock
we said another five and the last five were chanted before we
went home at 4 o'clock.

Every time the Teacher left the classroom she told us to say
aspirations. So anyone passing our room could hear 44 voices
chanting "Mother of God, pray for us. Virgin most pure protect
us". When she came backshe would ask how many we said. It
was a bit like an auction. Someone would start at 20 and the
bids would go up. One idiot once said 5,000. She got slaps.

The Teacher kept her books in a little press that was built

into the wall. This was locked every evening and she took the key home with her. I don't know who she thought was going to risk going to prison just to get their hands on a bundle of third class books.

My friend Eileen Gannon was in charge of the Teacher's books. Eileen was an only child so she always had lovely clothes not hand me downs like the rest of us. She had short fair hair which was always perfect. Even if she was out in a hurricane not one hair on her head would move.

She always knew her tables and spellings and when she recited her poem she never once had to look up at the ceiling for Divine Inspiration. She was the Teacher's Pet, that's why she was in charge of the books. I sat beside her and sometimes she helped me with my sums if the Teacher wasn't looking.

One morning, after the Rosary, Eileen collected the key and took Miss Griffins books from the press and put them on the table. We started with tables and spellings, then Gaeilge where we struggled with the Tuiseal Ginideach, Uimhir Iolra.

At 12 0'clock, religion time, Miss Griffin started searching through the bundle of books for her Catechism. We were all very familiar with this book. It had a purple crepe paper cover on it and it was bulging with holy pictures and relics. Miss griffin collected pieces of Saints bones and flesh and clothes and she impressed on us how sacred these were. Occasionally, if she judged someone to be beyond redemption she would make them kneel up on her desk and she would place a relic on their head.

Miss Griffin glared at Eileen and said "Where's my catechism?". Eileen ran to the press and searched but it was empty. The Teacher's face began to turn red and we began to quake.

"Who stole my Catechism?" she roared. I looked around to see if any hand was going up. There was silence.

"We have a thief and a liar in this class. Do you know what happens to thieves and liars?" We certainly did because she was always telling us. She even did a demonstration one day. She lit a candle and asked for a volunteer to put their finger into the flame so that we could experience what Hell might be like. We all shrank into our seats.

When she saw that she wasn't getting anywhere with her investigations, she decided to try the "softly, softly" approach. "I'll turn my back" she said "and whoever took my catechism can put it back on the table and there'll be no more about it". SILENCE.

The Mr. Nice Guy approach didn't last very long and she started ranting and raving and making us pray. Finally she said "that's it, I'm going to search everyone's bag. Put them up on the tables. "

She went down one row and emptied everyone's belongings onto the floor. As she was coming up my row the bell rang and we were mercifully released to go outside to have our lunches. I took my lunch box out of my bag and as I did what did I see only a small piece of purple crepe peeping out from between my books. My heart almost stopped.

Luckily my lunchbox was huge as my mother thought that if she didn't give me half a loaf for my lunch that I would die of malnutrition. I carefully stuffed the catechism into the lunchbox and ran to the toilets. I climbed up on the toilet bowl and pushed the book down behind the rusty cistern. The rest of the day passed in a haze of terror. I had to get rid of it somehow.

When the bell finally rang, I hurried to the toilet and retrieved the Catechism. I put it back into my bag and went home. My Mam was upstairs and there was a roaring fire in the grate. Without giving it too much thought I took out the catechism and threw it on the fire. I watched as the pages were eaten up by the flames and the Saints bones and flesh and clothes disappeared up the chimney. I was safe, no one could call me a liar and or a thief now.

The next day was Saturday when Mam marched us all up to the Church for weekly confession. I knelt in the small coffin like box waiting for the priest to slide back the little door. I couldn't see his face but I could hear him breathing. "Bless me Father for I have sinned. It's a week since my last confession. I stole the

Teacher's Catechism"

A tired or was it a bored voice said "Well, give it back and for your Penance say three Hail Marys." I left the confession box and slowly the enormity of what I had just done began to dawn on me. My conscience whispered, "You told a lie in confession."

"I did not"

"You told a lie of omission. That means you made a bad confession." My conscience seemed to have a Kerry accent.

"And when you make a bad confession, that's worse than a mortal sin. It's a sacrilege and you can't receive Holy Communion if you've committed a sacrilege because that would be another sacrilege."

What was I going to do now? My Mother made us go to Communion every Sunday and no excuses were accepted. Anyway, I couldn't tell her I had committed a sacrilege, she'd be horrified. I went to Holy Communion and now I had two sacrileges on my soul.

And so began a pattern. Every Saturday I confessed to stealing the catechism and the priest would tell me to give it back and on Sunday I went to Holy Communion. I don't know how many sacrileges a soul can take but mine must have been at breaking point.

Whatever about my soul, my mind was in turmoil and I began to have nightmares. They were usually about a dark ugly person hiding in either the wardrobe or under the bed. Night after night my poor mother would take me out of bed and show me that there was no one there and it was just a dream.

The situation got worse and I began to walk in my sleep. I was halfway down the road one night. I was always trying to escape. You didn't have to be Freud to know what was going on.

My mother decided to take me to the Doctor. He said that I probably had worms and he prescribed a tablespoonful of Castor Oil every night for a week. Well, if the mental torture didn't kill me the castor oil almost did the job. By the end of the week I was a shadow of my former self.

By now my Mother was at her wits end and she thought the only solution was to bring me up to the Parish Priest, Fr. Clarke.

He was a big jolly man with bushy eyebrows. He looked at me and said "I know what will fix you. I have a relic of St. Catherine Le Boure and it's been known to cure all sorts of ailments."

He took out a small glass box that contained a piece of bone and rubbed it up and down my face as he mumbled some prayers.I began to feel better instantly.I don't know whether it was a miracle or not but the nightmares and sleepwalking stopped and that was good enough for me.

Before Mam and I left the church I had a moment of Divine Inspiration. I told the priest that my teacher had lost her Catechism and all her relics and I asked him if he had any relics that I could give to her. He gave me a card with a piece of cloth from the robe of St. Margaret someone or other.

Next morning I courageously presented the relic to Miss Griffin. I could tell she was ecstatic because she almost smiled. I became the teacher's second pet and I was given the job of assisting Eileen Gannon to protect the teachers books. She couldn't have picked a better custodian.

THE REBEL HOMECOMING

By Phil MacSweeney,
Turner's Cross, Cork

Uncle Eddie's ashes were brought home to Cork to be scattered in his beloved Rebel city, but his wishes were met in a strange way

THE EXPLOITS of my pal Danny's mysterious Uncle Eddie, a resident of the United States of America, dominated our youthful activities. Forced to flee his native Cork in his younger days and not allowed to return, he was a permanent and a very reluctant exile. His subsequent life was full of misery, homesickness and loneliness (or so the story goes).

To our youthful gang he was a hero, a magical and mystical figure from whom parcels arrived at regular intervals. Many a scheme was thought up for smuggling him home.

As we grew older we realised that some deeper mystery existed. But to probe was not an option. It was obvious that Uncle Eddie was obsessed with the Rebel City and we could not but wonder why, if such a degree of loneliness existed, he did not return home even on holiday.

If the American parcels were to be taken as an assessment of wealth, there was no shortage of money and surely after such a period of time the fault for any misdemeanour cold be purged.

In early spring last year we noticed that Danny was becoming a little paranoid himself. Our weekly gatherings were concentrating more and more on the singing of Cork songs. We sincerely hoped this was only a phase and that it would soon pass.

Gradually the story emerged – Uncle Eddie's time on this life was nearing the end and Danny had promised that on his death he, Danny, would travel to America, bring home the ashes and scatter them over Cork city.

We knew then we were being groomed to perform.

In due course Uncle Eddie died and in accordance with his promise Danny, having put us all on standby, travelled to America and returned with a beautiful ornate urn of ashes.

Arrangements were already in place, made with his priest friend in the Holy Trinity Church. It was decided that after a blessing, the ashes would be scattered over the South Branch of the river Lee near to where Uncle Eddie was born.

We were assigned our positions. Andy on spoons would be on the top step of the quayside while the vocalists would be on the lower steps. The ceremony would commence with the singing of "Beautiful City" followed up by Mickey's recitation of "The Exile's Return" and the ceremony would conclude with a rendering of "The Banks."

While there was no question of reneging, we sincerely hoped we would not attract undue attention or become a public showcase. We were very conscious of he proximity of The Radio Eireann head offices. This could become front page news.

On the morning of the Scattering, Fr. Michael rang Danny telling him that he was scheduled to say the 10am mass. He suggested that Danny leave the Urn on the broad ledge at the end of the church, and attend the mass at which prayers would be said for Uncle Eddie. After mass the ashes would be blessed, we would take up our positions and the scattering would commence. This was agreed.

Giving the congregation time to leave the church, we all approached the Urn. It was exactly where Danny had placed it but to Danny's surprise it was now uncapped. He was perplexed but nothing could prepare him for what was to follow when it was discovered that no trace whatsoever could be found of the ashes themselves.

A distraught Danny could not be consoled. Having travelled all the way to America to collect Uncle Eddie's ashes he had now lost them in Cork.

ORIGINAL WRITING FROM IRELAND'S OWN 2013

Very gradually the probable truth dawned on Fr. Michael. It was Ash Wednesday, people had assumed that the Urn contained blessed ashes and had taken them home.

EPILOGUE: Uncle Eddie's wish was fulfilled, his ashes were certainly scattered all over Cork City and we were deprived of our moment of musical glory.

48

ACRES OF GUILT

By John Patrick Bell,
Manorhamilton, Co. Leitrim

*Times are really tough on the farm, with the bad weather causing
serious problems. There is not enough work and the farmer has to
let go his hard-working helper, Eoin, from up the mountain*

THE RATTLE of the wind through the farmyard reminded
me of another dawn - a dawn long ago, a bleak grey
dawn without promise or hope, the mountain black
against a leaden sky. Such days had passed through our lives
that year, each as dark as the next, strung together like black
beads on a rosary.

The rattle of the farmyard pump had awakened us both; "Is
that Eoin?" my wife had asked, "God! That man would shame
us all". She had jumped out of bed, her feet slapping on the
cold floor.

"Have you not told him yet?" she reminded me.

"Not yet", I said, looking out of the window wishing I had.
The broad back of Eoin bent over the pump, at his feet the
black and white collie his constant shadow.

That was a year I would rather forget, a summer without
two days of sunshine to fuse together. Barley and oats rotted on
the stalks and that which hadn't was not worth the harvesting.
When the sun did shine it was only to lift our hopes dashing
them down again in yet another downpour on the wet earth.

Afraid at the price of winter feed, I had sold the store cattle. It
proved a wise move, a wet summer into a wet autumn; a bad year
running its course with many's a farmers' curse upon its back.

But I would survive, our stout slated farmhouse and its acres
said we would. My wife stirred me from my thoughts.

"You should have him told after the hay was got in," she said getting annoyed.

Was it sorry or guilt, I felt for the man? Not a personal guilt for I had kept him in work most of the year, but in such a bad year finding him a full day's work wasn't easy.

Much of the work I could have managed myself, but anything to give that proud man a day's pay. Sometimes I lingered in bed trying to plan our days work, Eoin Mor was no fool and would think the less of me if the tasks were too few, and a long litany of tasks they were too, stretching back to the spring.

Like the weeks he had spent whitewashing both inside and out any man-made structure about the place, including the farmhouse itself. Now the haymaking was over for another year, half of it still rotting in the wet fields. The barley field was cleared and raked for next spring's ploughing.

"Let him finish the milking then bring him in for his breakfast", I said motioning her towards the stairs. That last morning I remember it well, for work had run out for Eoin Mor; there was no contract or obligation between us for Eoin was his own man, as free as the mountain he lived on.

In other years when bigger money had called, Eoin would take himself off for weeks at a time, building work or farm work was all the same to him, his strong back doing the work of two men. A day's labour for a day's pay; no stamp or tax to the state, expecting nothing in return. Such was his way, a noble way, a proud way, no man's claim upon his back.

He had come in as usual for his breakfast, the dog at his feet.

'Dia's Mhuire dhuit," giving his blessing as he took his place at the table.

God and Mary indeed! Had those black days hardened my heart? Was there nothing more I could have done? After all these years there is still guilt; our rich fields ensured our survival; our planted mark upon the land. Somehow the words came, I avoided his honest gaze, and he'd taken it calmly enough, consoling me in my dilemma.

I mentioned the new benefits that the state was introducing and the winter relief schemes.

He would make inquiries the next time he was the length of the town, he said, but not very convincingly. For Eoin was not one for the filling in of forms or making a poor mouth, the "Beal Bhoct," as he called it.

My wife had made up a parcel of tea and sugar begging him to accept it for his trouble, I had pressed a few pounds into his hands, calling it severance pay to placate his pride and perhaps my own guilt. Uneasy with our generosity, he arose from the table, a last look around the kitchen and he walked to the door.

"If the wind veers to the nor east, there'll be an early winter," he said. We both shook hands and he thanked me

"Come spring I will have more work for you, the early ploughing," I said reminding him again of government help. He pondered on a few sources of possible work, MacCafferty the builder was taking on men and the week before at the market cross hadn't Kerrigan offered him work there and then. "So don't worry yourself, young fellow," he reassured me 'There's work for them that want it".

But for all his talk, I thought I noticed a weariness come over him, a last blessing before bracing himself for his steep walk home.

Eoin Mor was right; the snows came early that year, a relief after the incessant rain, a snowy mantle and clear blue sky returning beauty to the glen. A soft hush descended unbroken except for the odd lorry or car labouring to the village.

The early snow put paid to Eoin's hopes of finding work, my guilt at laying him off rising to meet his likely frustration; no school or chapel bell beckoned Eoin or his kin off the mountain. The snow lay long that year, for it was well into its second month before his lads approached. Pulling an old wooden sleigh, the collie in tow, they slid and pulled their way down the mountain.

Eoin sent his regards and apart from a few shortages such as potatoes, all was well but the gaunt look on their young faces told me more than Eoin was letting on. Well, we filled that sleigh, half emptying our own food cupboard, and another bag of praties to keep her weighted down, I had joked, bringing a smile to their serious faces.

As they left Phelim, his eldest, turned and tied the collie to the old farm pump,

"You're to keep the collie," he shouted. Cursing the man for I didn't want his dog; yet I couldn't refuse, I could not shame him, untying the collie I brought it in.

She would not eat, at night her mournful howls travelled the length of the glen. On the fourth morning I slipped the lead and off she tore up the mountain; with the rope still in my hand I realised my mistake! Sending his collie was not without sacrifice. Eoin's decision to give the dog was dictated by his poverty and an attempt to hold on to his self –respect. Much as he loved that dog, he valued his pride even more.

By releasing the dog I had refused the poor man's offering, Eoin wouldn't understand, I had rejected his gift, not any gift but something close, a part of him and his ways. The real gap between us was not one of religion or ancestry, simply the age old gap between the landowner and the landless, the rich and the poor, the haves and the have-nots.

Days later Eoin passed the house, a wild look on his face, hurried plans afoot, hungry men can't afford to be patient

One morning long ago it all came to an end. Down they came off the mountain, dark forms against the white snow. Eoin led the way, unbalanced by the heavy suitcase he shouldered, his wife, her long skirts catching the trodden snow, clutching the youngest to her side. More children followed, four or was it five? Their poverty wrapped up in brown paper parcels. Searching for words, useless words, we ran to meet them and brought them into the warmth.

A car was on its way from Derry, where they would stay the night, the next day the boat to Adrossan in Scotland, Eoin explained.

"My sister will meet us," his wife said, her tired eyes wandering over the comforts of the house.

"There will be another war in Europe," said he, as if I hadn't heard. "So there'll be plenty of work in the Glasgow shipyards, sure the people are all leaving the uplands," he said, waving his hands towards the mountains to further justify his going.

The chug of a car's engine and the squeal of brakes in the snow broke the lapsed silence between us. The children scrambled out of the house and into the car, their thin faces pressed against the windows with wonder and excitement.

"And the collie dog?" I inquired, curious at its absence. He finished tying the case to the back of the car before answering. "I drowned it last Sunday above in the Lough." Aware of my stunned silence he offered an explanation, easing his large frame into the car.

"She belonged on the mountain - no good for anywhere else," giving me a long hard look before slamming the car door.

I was going to reply, "She belonged to you Eoin Mor, no good for anyone else," but it was all over and words would not have lessened Eoin's hurt or my guilt.

THE SUMMER HOLIDAYS

MJ DOHERTY,
Inishowen, Co. Donegal

Ann is sent to share her Summer holidays with her grandmother and her Aunt Philomena, and this opens up a new world to her

O N A COLD DAY in the spring of 1959, a black car arrived at our hill farm. It was driven by my uncle Patrick who was home on holidays from Australia. He hired a car and brought my grandmother and aunt Philomena to visit my estranged mother. I had to run down the fields to tell my father about the visitors. But he said; "there's work to be done". He kept his head down and continued working with my brothers beside him in the fields. He didn't let the boys go up to meet their relations.

The old woman tried to make peace with my mother, suggesting she bring the children to visit during the school holidays. Obstinate as always, my mother refused, saying she would be far too busy. But then she looked at me and said "Ann should go to see that part of the county". Aunt Philomena said "the house will be quiet when Patrick goes back to Sydney, Ann could spend the summer holidays with us".

The following July, my mother took me to Derry on a Lough Swilly bus to hand me over to my aunt. "Look at the style of her", my mother said as Philomena approached us. She was beautifully dressed in a green floral dress with a matching cardigan. She wore brown high-heeled shoes. Her red lipstick was the same colour as her nail varnish. Her lovely auburn hair was pinned up showing off her gold earrings. A faint smell of perfume drifted from her. My mother and aunt didn't look like sisters.

The pair did some shopping in Littlewoods Stores. Dazzled by the array of goods, I got lost in the maze of counters but I was quickly dragged back by my mother. She wasn't too cross and bought me dates as a treat. I loved the sticky, sweet, fruity taste. Refusing the offer of tea, my mother rushed off home, leaving me with Aunt Philomena. I felt excited but scared.

We went to a little café. Everything appeared to be coloured brown and white and had a strong smell of coffee and sugar. Mirrors with pictured sketched on them lined the walls. Dainty white cups sat on saucers with tiny paper mats. The side plates had white lacy mats a few sizes bigger. "Those are called 'doilies', Philomena said. We drank tea and ate tasty little triangle sandwiches without any crusts. I put the paper mats up my sleeve and took them with me to use again.

Philomena bought some magazines for herself and some crayons and a colouring book for me. With time to kill we looked in shop windows until the bus came. My favourite windows had big dolls dressed up like people in them Philomena called the dolls 'mannequins'. She pointed out the Indian ladies, wearing their beautiful saris.

To a seven year old child from the countryside, the city was amazing. The streets were crowded with people hurrying along. The parade of shops and tall buildings all joined together. The noise of the traffic speeding past was alien to me, being used to clean mountain air, I didn't like the smell of petrol and coal smoke. It made me feel like coughing.

Upstairs on the double decker bus, my aunt settled down to read her magazines. To me, she looked like someone out of a magazine. We travelled for miles through the countryside and past small villages. Branches of the tall trees scratched at the windows of the bus as it rattled along the bumpy road. Slowly, the landscape began to change. The hills faded into the background and the sea appeared. A smell of salt and seaweed filled the bus.

Eventually the bus stopped at a small town where most people got off. We went on past the black and white tower of the lighthouse. I knew the lighthouse from a picture we had on the wall at home. The bus stopped again at a pub. "This is our stop," Aunt Philomena said. We walked a good distance towards an old two-storey house. As we made our way up the path, a crop of pink roses swaying on the bushes in the strong sea breeze gave off a heavy fragrance.

My grandmother was dressed in black, sitting in a high armchair beside a big black range, glowing orange with a turf fire. Kettles and pots hissed at the side of the range. I gulped down a bowlful of creamy porridge served to me by my grandmother. It tasted good and I would have liked some more but Philomena instructed me to get ready for bed and then took me upstairs to my room.

The room seemed vast in contrast to my tiny box room in our small farmhouse. It had a high ceiling and a big window. The cream wallpaper was speckled with tiny pink and green flowers. A faded rug covered most of the wooden floor. I recognised the scent of lavender polish from the heavy brown furniture. Near the window, there stood a dressing table with three mirrors and six small drawers. Beside it was a chair with a worn red velvet seat.

Miniature pictures of people who seemed slightly familiar sat on a long white cloth covering the dressing table. On the wall, hung a picture of a stern looking man in uniform and another of a big ship. A huge bed with brass knobs dominated the room. Two fat pillows peeped out from under a patchwork quilt.

"Say your prayers and get into bed", instructed Philomena. Obediently, I did as she said. The bed was almost too high to climb into. "You must be tired so have a good sleep now", said my aunt. Then she closed the curtains and left the room. Left alone, I felt very small in the big quiet room.

For a while I slept soundly until I began to have nightmares. I dreamt that the branches of the trees broke the windows of the bus and almost scratched my eyes out; the man in the picture was angry with me; I tried to escape but I found myself falling down, down, down...

I woke up as I fell out of the bed and hit the rug with a thump.

The room was totally dark. All the emotions I had bottled up throughout the day exploded. I began to scream at the top of my voice, the piercing cries cutting the stillness of the night. My Aunt Philomena came running in.

"Stop! stop screaming at once. You'll give my mother a heart attack, stop, do you hear me? Stop, please stop!" she pleaded as my screams grew louder and louder. My mother was a firm believer in discipline. She would have given me a choice; to stop screaming or get a good slapping and I would have known to shut up. But my sophisticated aunt was unable to silence me.

Finally, Grandmother called out "bring her downstairs". A frail figure shivering in her nightdress and shawl, she raked the fire and threw on some turf. My screams turned to sobs; I didn't want to give her a heart attack. She sat me down in a chair and said to me, "now Ann, tell me what is troubling you". I told her every thought that came into my head. "I'm afraid of the angry man in the picture and that my father will go to hell for being a protestant", I said.

"We'll take away your grandfather's picture and as for your father going to hell; sure only bad people go to hell", Granny said gently.

"Mammy won't come here because she hasn't got nice things to wear like Philomena", I sobbed. "Your mother can't be spending money on fancy clothes when she has children to keep. She will come here when she is ready", she replied.

"The room's too dark" I whimpered. The old woman nodded wisely.

"Take her back to bed and get her a night light. Remove that picture; sure we don't want him driving Ann away too", she told Philomena. "Tomorrow we'll search the house for a couple of porcelain dolls and a wee tea-set for you to play with", Granny said to me. Philomena lit a tiny glass lamp. It winked at me from the mantelpiece.

"There you are, Ann, the room's brighter now", said a relieved Philomena. All my fears melted away and I couldn't wait until morning to play with the dolls and the tea-set.

My Aunt Philomena worked part-time in the library. She loved reading. On Friday mornings, she worked in the post office. Soon, I began to help with the housework. I picked blackberries and gooseberries for jam-making. "Ann's a great wee worker for all the size of her" Granny said. On sunny days we went to the shore. Sometimes we gathered dulse and carrageen moss. If the tide was safe, we went swimming. Splashing about in the sea, with the taste of salt on my lips and the gentle waves lapping over me; I wished the holidays would never end.

I met Jack on my second summer. He was a deep-sea fisherman and kept coming in and out of Philomena's life. He made her laugh and gave her a ring shaped like a snake with diamonds for eyes. Jack charmed her with stories of fishing around the Costa do Marisco, the Shellfish Coast in Galicia in the North of Spain. From Jack, I learned about Saint James and the medieval pilgrims scattering scallop shells along the way to Santiago de Compostela. I gathered shells and day dreamed of going on the Pilgrimage.

Those were happy days! We went lobster fishing in Jack's small boat. He brought us to his cottage. It was painted blue and white; the colours of the sea. Jack boiled two lobsters alive. Philomena made a big salad with lettuce and scallions straight from Jack's garden. They sprinkled the salad with Spanish olive oil and vinegar. The three of us feasted on the delicious food although the cruelty to the lobsters bothered me.

Granny didn't like Jack. She would talk to herself about him saying; "that bloody Jack, he'll never settle down. The sea calls him and he has to answer. When his money's spent or if he gets fed up, off he goes. She's wasting her time on him. She needs a home of her own".

On my third and last summer holiday at my grandmother's house, the sea had called Jack again. This time he went to the east coast of America where the fishing industry was booming. He hoped to work on the big American boats and make enough money to build a new house. Philomena was busy caring for my grandmother who had fallen and broken her hip. She couldn't afford to give up her job and was glad of my help.

We didn't have much fun that year. At nighttime I shared in

the 'Adventures of the Famous Five' while Philomena read 'Tess of the D'Urbervilles' and wept for the heroine. The clock on the mantelpiece ticked the time away. Philomena was tired and lonely. I hoped Jack would come back soon and marry her.

But early in January of the following year; the sea claimed Jack for its own. His boat sank in a storm off Canada. His body was never found. A few months later, my grandmother had a heart attack and passed away. My Uncle Patrick inherited the house and returned from Australia with his family to live there. Philomena went to London to another aunt whom I never met.

I never saw Philomena again. She died a few years later. My mother said that Philomena always read too much and couldn't live in the real world. But I thought she was like a character out of one of her novels. A young woman trapped in a lonely house by the sea waiting for her lover who never returned. Like all the great heroines, she went to join him in another dimension.

THE RED SHOES

By Elizabeth Waterhouse,
Mullingar, Co. Westmeath

*The arrival of the American parcel causes great excitement and I
lost my heart to a pair of the most exquisite shoes I had ever seen*

THEY WERE exquisite, made from the softest most
delicate red crimson leather. They were round toed and
had a three-inch heel. They were meant for petite young
feet and they drew me to them like tiny magnets. I had to have
them. Fifty years later I can still recall the sensual aroma of
expensive leather, and feel the heartrending longing to put
them on my 14 years old feet.

It was late 1962 and I was staying at my grandmother's
home in the midlands for the long, hot summer. Us children
were eagerly awaiting the arrival of the postman. We were
listening intently for the click click of his overburdened bike as
he made his way over the hill near grandma's house.

We had collectively stood on the brow of the hill every
morning for the past week, hoping that the postman would
bring the American parcel from Aunt Marie with its treasure
trove of costume jewellery, silky bits of lingerie, bits of this and
that, shoes, skirts, big flouncy blouses, odd bits of ribbon and
the smell of camphor balls.

Our excitement was explosive as the little pudgy, red faced
postman's head appeared over the hill.

We almost knocked him off his bike trying to extract the
huge parcel from him, and he cycled off, a bit lighter in weight
and spirit too. He would get his reward of a tot of whiskey
from Gran for his trouble.

Taking the parcel into Gran's kitchen we plonked it onto

the table. She refused to let us open it until we had the dishes washed and the kitchen spick and span. The dishes got the quickest wash and dry in living memory.

Once the wrapping was carefully opened such a treasure trove of bits and pieces was revealed. Silky lacy knickers, skirts and cardigans, shoes and boots, sheer nylons and wonderful chunky pieces of jewellery and gold gleaming watches. It seemed like all of our Christmases had come at once.

Now matching bits of everything, rings, watches, bangles and bracelets that almost pulled our small wrists apart with their weight, necklets that almost stopped the blood in the jugular veins and watches that had long ago emitted their last tick or tock, held us spellbound as we delved in like vultures after dead carrion.

Aunt Marie had married a jeweller and had worked in Watherbury, Connecticut, in a little shop for all of her long life. Loads of junk my mother called out as she watched us in disbelief. "If it was any good she wouldn't have sent it," she said sardonically.

To us, however, they were beautiful and sparkly and made us feel like royalty.

Dripping with half the contents of a small jewellers shop in Waterbury, Connecticut, dressed in flimsy knickers that ended up around our ankles, where the strength of the elastic was questionable, and with floral A-line skirts and baggy sweaters, we danced around like small clowns in a circus. Just then some delicate folds of flimsy paper caught my eye. Carefully unwrapping it, I exposed the exquisite red shoes.

The smell of leather pervaded my senses, the beauty of the styling and the feel and touch made my heart beat faster. I lifted them carefully.Lifting my foot in the air, I pulled them on.

They fitted like a glove, enclosing my feet in comfort and warmth. I felt like Cinderella in her glass slippers.

My mother spoilt the moment, "Take those shoes off, you little rap," she shouted."They can go to Pegeen, poor Pegeen could do with a new pair of shoes."

"What!" I felt like I was struck by a claw hammer. "Pegeen

is old. She's got old fat feet. It's sacrilege to give them to her to ruin. She will drop ash on them. They're meant for dancing," I shouted in dismay.

"Enough," my mother made a fruitless swing at me, missing me by a hare's breadth, as I dodged and ducked and skipped through the open doorway like Margot Fonteyn in Swan Lake. I was quicker than her. I ran through the farmyard, jumping over chickens, hens, goslings, puppies and other squawkers and squealers as I danced my way towards the bottoms. "Catch me if you can."

I could still hear my mother wittering on above the farmyard din. "I'll kill that one when I get my hands on her. She won't sit on her posterior for a week."

I laughed with sheer joy, "Yeah, yeah, yeah." I danced through the bottoms and skipping joyfully among dung heaps, hay bales, junk bits of farm machinery and finally lush green grass. I headed towards Nut Wood to pick nuts and blackberries. I filled up my deep pockets, and enjoying the fresh air and privacy, and posing shamelessly in my new found treasure.

I was Cinderella, the Queen of Sheba, Aladdin and Ali Baba, floating through the air on my magic carpet, skipping puddles, gliding over rocks and pirouetting all over the dark sunbeam riddled confines of Nut Wood.

The wind on my face, the sensual smell of leather and the weight of the American jewellers shop finally wore me out and it was time to return and pay the piper.

My mother was waiting at the hall door, with a look on her face that would ignite world wars.

This time she caught me. She wrestled me onto her knee, and unceremoniously wrenched the red treasure from my feet.

I was sent to bed, without tea and relieved of my jewellers shop. I longed for those shoes, cried myself to sleep dreaming about them.

I didn't know it then but it symbolised the change from childhood to adulthood. I have searched all my life for similar shoes that looked, fitted and smelled like them. I've never managed to find anything remotely like them.

They symbolised youth, beauty and sensuality and a long hot summer's day from a youth that I can never recapture.

HIGHLY COMMENDED

AFTER THE STORM

By Mary D'Arcy,
Malone Road, Belfast

A moment later a boy with a satchel crashed into the room. There was an audible intake of air as Miss Viney's eye fell on him like a searchlight. She tapped her fork against her plate

"OH, NO, let her not be coming this way." Nessa left off cleaning her window to peer at the black-clad figure hobbling towards her down the street. "She's taken offence and wants to let me know it. How narrow-minded, petty. But ... maybe it isn't her."

Throwing down her chamois, Nessa flew from the window and rummaged through her cupboards. Not for a while did her husband's binoculars come to hand. Back at the window, she focused them hurriedly and her heart sank down to her boots. For – yes. Just what she feared. Her. Pointing this way. Passing the rows of houses with studied indifference. Eyes fixed straight ahead. One hand gripping her cane. And in the other – Oh, dear Lord.

Nessa heaved a martyred sigh. As if Hurricane Debbie having three days earlier taken the lives of eleven people, uprooted trees, ripped slates from every roof, caused Jarlath's bus to skid and shake up all his pilgrims – as if all this were not enough, here now was yet more grief in the shape of the tetchiest female in the town.

With a face as hard as iron, Nessa set down the binoculars, re-hung her curtains and checked the pie in the Stanley range. By which time her ears picked up the click at her gate followed by the dragging strides that distinguished the lame Miss Viney. Next came three loud raps on the door.

Nessa braced herself for battle. In a background such as hers – civil servants in the main – a circle into which neither brawling nor misconduct had ever entered, there was something peculiarly distasteful about the presence of a querulous neighbour. On the other hand, she reflected, it might be just Miss Viney's age. She's old, alone, abrasive, and doesn't understand our ways. Why not treat her gently and make light of what poor Darragh did? After all, he meant no harm.

But, oh, to think of her sallying up through the longest street in Craigdoran, the neighbours guessing her destination, seeing what she clutched in her hand.

The knocks sounded once again. Untying the strings of her apron, Nessa hurried to the door.

"Well, hello," she said, with the air of someone pleased to be paid a visit.

Iris Viney stood there, staring at her without expression. A wisp of a woman with a long limp neck and large pessimistic eyes, there was that about her lower face that suggested – as Jarlath once unkindly remarked - a soft leather purse with a hard tight clasp.

"What a surprise. Won't you come in?"

Miss Viney hesitated. Behind her, the street was holding its breath. Curtains twitched. Pascal Egan, up on his ladder supposedly fixing his roof tiles, had long since left off hammering. The Maloney twins abandoned a game of hopscotch to watch beyond their garden gate. A neighbour emerged, and found things to do in her garden.

Everything stood still. Then the turret clock in the small church tower broke the spell by striking three.Darragh would soon be home from school, and oh – why, why did he have to call on Miss Viney?

From somewhere Nessa trawled up a smile. "Come along," she said. "The kettle is whistling."

Her manner, as she held back the door, showed nothing of the chaos of sensations which writhed within her. Tread carefully. It will all blow over – like Hurricane Debbie.

In the kitchen, she motioned her visitor into a chair. Miss

Viney stayed on her feet.

Slewing around, she plonked a bottle down on the table causing the water inside it to swirl. Nessa glanced at the bottle and felt her colour rising. A plastic container in the shape of the Virgin Mary, its bright blue cap was fashioned into a little crown. Darragh had bought it the day before.

Nessa looked up from the table. "Miss Viney," she began, but the other held up a detaining hand. "Why, in the name of heaven, am I always Miss Viney to everyone? I do have a first name in case it escaped your notice. Iris."

Nessa raised her chin then lowered it, as though a great mystery had now been solved. "Very good," she said. "But look, it's a long walk from Riverview and I think you ought to at least sit down."

That's it. Be firm. Just like herself. "And here," she added, "give me your coat."

Miss Viney hesitated. "What I came to say –"

"Come along," said Nessa, holding out her hand. Iris Viney, to her surprise, allowed herself to be shelled of her coat. Then, with the aid of her cane, she lowered herself onto a chair and rested her arm on the table.

"The reason I'm here, Mrs Whyte –"

"I, too, have a first name," said Nessa, as she hung the coat on the back of the door. Then, with an ironic glance in Miss Viney's direction, she grabbed a towel, took the pie from the oven and carried it across to the table, scattering a delicious fragrance.

"It's Nessa. And you're going to have some apple pie." And with that, she took down crockery, pulled out cutlery, made tea, found milk, sugar and cream and drew up a chair across from her visitor.

Miss Viney sat in stony silence, her eye on the holy water which Nessa had moved to the end of the table. But the pie, the tea, and the delicious aromas had the effect of restoring her to speech.

"Well, I'm bound to admit I have never tasted anything better."

"That's because the apples are good." Nessa held out the

cream jug. "If you remember, I got them in your place. Which reminds me, who's looking after the shop?"

Miss Viney chewed for a moment, then a sheepish look came into her eyes. "I closed it for an hour or two." She slopped more cream across her pie. "And I've a good mind, now I'm seventy, to close it altogether."

"That would be a pity," said Nessa. "The shop is a landmark. And you yourself an institution."

It was true. Everyone liked Miss Viney's shop. An old-world grocery, established in the 1880s, it looked like nothing so much as the stage set for a Sean O'Casey play. Here, amid posters for Bovril and sacks of potatoes and meal, you could use Miss Viney's pay phone, buy stamps, a single cigarette, a cup of sugar, half a block of ice-cream.

On Saturdays, young Darragh would give a hand sprinkling sawdust on the floor, shifting boxes, stacking shelves – his reward a florin and a bar or two of chocolate.

"I'd be lost without him," Miss Viney would say.

In rare bursts of confidence she would relay to certain selected customers that she could easily do the work herself, but liked having young folks around her. But what she really should do - now that Time had finally caught up with her - was sell the business and join those neighbours who regularly went on bus tours.

There was something half-embarrassed, half-apologetic in her way of voicing this avowal as if she didn't expect you to take her seriously.

But, oh, she would sigh, to sit back in a bus and see all the different towns, instead of withering away in your shop until Death the Deliverer paid you a visit.

"Institution or not," she was saying now, "I ought to clock off, only I can't."

"And why not," asked Nessa, "if you want to."

"Because," said Miss Viney, "without the shop, few would ever come near me. And why would they – a crabby old lady like me?"

"That's not true," said Nessa, but without conviction.

"Perfectly true, and you know it."

There followed an excruciating silence. Nessa consulted the clock and gave a sidelong glance at the holy water. "Do I take it ... Darragh upset you?"

Somebody's voice asked the question. A voice which sounded unfamiliar. Nessa could not have recognised it as her own. So tense had she suddenly become she couldn't have recognised anything, for Darragh was ambling down the street kicking a stone before him.

"Yes and no." Miss Viney set down her fork. "As I say, I'm seventy. I'll be seventy-one on the ninth of October. A lone woman. Of a different persuasion to the rest of the town. My circle of friends reduced to five – the vicar, his wife, and my cousins in Cork."

"Nonsense," said Nessa, "everyone in town is your friend."

"Can you imagine," carried on Iris, as though her hostess hadn't spoken, "what it's like to see everyone else with families around them? Everyone else enjoying socials? Your neighbours from up and down the streets piling into busses – for years the old McManus tour bus, and now your husband's Whyte Line bus. Taking off on what you call pilgrimages and I call tours?"

"Oh, but Iris – "

"Yourself among them. And your son."

Something flared up behind Nessa's eyes, but she quickly extinguished it. "We mostly go in summer, Iris. And not always on pilgrimages either. Darragh has cousins who live ..."

Nessa's voice trailed away for Miss Viney, she saw, was no longer listening. She was staring at the Stanley range where ash from the burning turf was sifting down between the bars. She seemed lost and absorbed in her gloomy thoughts.

"The Healys next door," she said at length. "The O'Briens in the bakery. The Quigleys. The Flynns. Taking off twice a year. Doing it for decades. And yesterday," she lifted her eyes and glared into Nessa's, "yesterday was the first time – ever – that anyone thought to bring me something from their holy place."

Nessa sat up electrified. Bring her back something? Had she

heard her right? She would have ... wanted something from the shrine?

Her gaze went to the holy water, then to Miss Viney. Was this, then, her real gripe – a sense of being excluded?

And what about Darragh? Nessa inwardly quailed. To think she'd rounded on her son for presenting someone not of their faith with a bottle of holy water. Shame on her. Shame.

"One young boy," carried on Iris. "A child of ten. The only person in the town ever to include me in anything. All these years I've been on the outside looking in."

"But that's not true," cried Nessa, her eyes troubled. "Who called round to you while the storm was raging? Who were the people who put sandbags against your doors? Who at this very moment is checking out the roof of your church? Us. The neighbours you imagine don't give a toss.`

Iris was mutinous. "Still doesn't mean I'm not an outsider."

Nessa touched a hand to her brow in a gesture of patient suffering. "Miss Viney," she said. "Iris. Listen to me. Think. Think back over the years. To the time your brother died. Your sister. Your aunt in the draper's – Lilian? Who were the people who piled into your church to pay their respects? Who were the people stood by their graves, sent flowers, and notes of condolence? Who drove you to hospital that time you fell and broke your wrist? Who offers you lifts to Cork, and calls on you every Christmas? Who –"

"All right, said Iris. "All right, all right."

"Us, Iris. Us. The people in the town you wrongly imagine are keeping you out."

Nessa drew a shaky breath. "Craigdoran is the smallest town in the midlands. Three thousand inhabitants. Everyone knows everyone else. We are One Big Family. Can't you see that, Iris? There are other grocers in town, and surely people flocking to Viney's is proof, if ever it were needed, you are more than one of us? Outsider indeed."

"Well –"A faint smile broke on the other's lips. "I suppose that's put me in my box."

It was all she got to say, for at that moment the front door opened and noisily closed again. "Ma, I'm home," came the piping treble.

A moment later a boy with a satchel crashed into the room. He drew up abruptly on seeing the visitor. There was an audible intake of air as Miss Viney's eye fell on him like a searchlight. She tapped her fork against her plate.

"I have been waiting for you, Darragh Whyte."

Colour came into the young boy's cheeks. He looked from Miss Viney to his mother and back.

"That gift you brought me yesterday," said Iris, pointing with her fork towards the end of the table. "I will have you know it all but fractured my finger."

Darragh stood silent, his colour mounting, for Miss Viney appeared to be livid.

"You know very well my hands are stiff. Yet you took off yesterday without loosening the cap. Loosening caps is one of the reasons I sometimes employ you. And so –let you loosen it now and pass it over."

She turned to Nessa and addressed her angrily. "Holy water is good. Gives you a sense of being blessed. Of being taken care of."

On the ninth day of October, three weeks after Hurricane Debbie sobbed up and down the country, the Whyte Line bus took off from Craigdoran at 8.45 in the morning.

Its passengers chattered. Among them was Iris who sat at the front, and found, to her great dismay, she couldn't quite enjoy the trip.

Everyone was gibbering at once, wishing her many happy returns, presenting her with silly gifts – imagine giving chocolates to someone who sells them? - pointing out landmarks, vying with each other to be the one to show the `new girl` round the shrine whenever - and if ever – Jarlath Whyte would speed it up and get them there.

ACROSS THE CAR-ROAD

By Elizabeth Brennan,
Castlecomer, Co. Kilkenny

Alice had tried to put the break-up with Mick behind her, but every time her older brother came to visit he brought up the subject again, stirring painful memories

WILSON ARMITRAGE stood with his back to the open log fire on which hung the bake pot with the twigs on top smouldering and slowly turning to white ash. He pulled on the pipe which he held in his right hand, smacking his lips with each draw of air. His eyes followed his sister about the kitchen. He watched her in her apron, her short, straight hair tied back with hair grips and noticed the few stray grey ones beginning to show at her temples. She was no longer young, he thought, the care lines of hard work were clearly visible, but, now and then, he could see the light in her eyes, the lovely smile which filled her face.

"We'll have a mug of tea now, and then I'll be off to the High Meadow. The weather's up for a few days and we must make the best of it. It'll be good to have that meadow down before the weekend."

Alice took the mugs from the dresser and brought the milk jug from the dairy, cut two thick slices of currant cake and smothered them with soft yellow butter.

"That'll keep you going until 4 o'clock, Wilson. I'll bring you up a gallon of tea then."

It was difficult for her here, Wilson thought, just the two of them since their mother died some few years ago. She had nursed their mother in her last illness and their father too, putting her own life on hold. Her heart was broken, he knew, when Mick Eardley had told her that she had to make up her mind. He wasn't going to wait for her for years, he said. And she had decided. She chose to stay with her mother, letting her chance of a home and family of her own go by.

Alice busied herself clearing up after the dinner, putting the potato skins in the pig-bucket and shaking the tablecloth outside the door. Taking the tin basin from behind the water bucket in the corner, she poured some boiling water from the heavy cast-iron kettle on the hob into it and cooled it with a mug of cold water from the bucket. One by one, she took the two blue-rimmed dinner plates, two mugs and the knives and forks, washed and dried them and replaced them on the dresser.

"I suppose we'll have himself tomorrow for the dinner. He seems to be making a habit of it now on Wednesdays," Wilson drawled in his high-pitched voice, having temporarily removed the pipe from his mouth.

Alice didn't answer. She bit her lip and a frown crossed her forehead. She quickened her pace because today was churning day and she was in a hurry to get to the dairy and get started. She had earlier left the buckets of cream and the buckets of water for swilling the churn ready.

Himself was her older brother, Baldi, a bachelor farmer from Ballinamona, two parishes away. When she and her sister, Ruby, were small they had called him Baldi, unable to pronounce his proper name, Archibald. She remembered how he teased them unmercifully and was always ready to tell tales on them, oftentimes getting them into trouble with their father. He had inherited some money after his father's death and had bought a farm and moved out, to the delight of her mother who had despaired of him ever doing any work.

At first he was very busy in the new farm cutting hedges, draining fields and getting into livestock. The novelty of the farm and responsibility soon wore off. He discovered that it was all hard work and, after a few years, set the land and lived on its earnings. Occasionally, he would make a visit home, not out of great love but to catch up on family and local news. However, lately he had started coming regularly and even stayed overnight, bringing a bag of dirty washing on the back of the bike and his good shoes for polishing.

Alice dreaded these visits. "No one showing any interest in you, Alice, since Mick Eardley changed his mind. He's rearing two fine sons up there now with Ellen Dargan. You're not getting any younger and you won't get a husband looking after Wilson."

Every time he visited, he managed to bring the subject up again. His words hurt. She had tried to put the memory of the break-up with Mick behind her. She didn't regret her decision, but the memory was painful.

"As we predicted, Alice, I see himself coming across the car-road,' Wilson announced next day just before dinner time. 'He's getting mighty fond of us, although now that he's here he might give a hand to turn the hay in the High Meadow."

The old sheepdog got up and wagged his tail. The iron gate into the yard creaked and they heard the bang of the bicycle against the wall.

"I hope you put my name in the pot, Alice," he shouted, as he threw a large bag on the settle bed.

Silently, Alice took another place-setting from the dresser, noisily placing the extra cutlery and blue-rimmed plate on the table.

"The first of our own potatoes today, Baldi, they're balls of flour after the last few weeks of fine weather," said Wilson as Alice served the dinner of home-cured bacon, potatoes and buttery green cabbage.

"Nothing like them to put hair on your chest," answered Baldi as he pushed the loose potato skins to the side of his plate.

Baldi licked his lips as he finished the last forkful of potatoes and took a last swig out of the tin mug of buttermilk. "That was a fine dinner, Alice. The best. Mick Eardley missed out. I doubt if Ellen Dargan can cook as well as you."

"Give it a rest, Baldi. That's all in the past and, anyway, it's none of your business. Wilson and myselfare happy here and if you can't think of anything else to talk about when you come, don't bother coming'

"Oh, suit yourself. To change the subject, since you're becoming so touchy, I was thinking of putting my place up for sale. It's coming up to the winter and it's a lonely station over there in Ballinamona with neither chick nor child near me. What'd ye think?"

"Aye, I suppose you're right about the loneliness," answered Wilson. 'Would you not think of moving into town for the winter? I hear there's plenty of accommodation available. You could go back to your own place in the spring."

"It was only a thought. I'll probably forget about it when the time comes. Still, with Alice here showing no sign of making a move she might as well look after two as one. There's plenty of room here. I brought over a bit of washing there, Alice. Just a few shirts and socks and my good shoes for church on Sunday in the shopping bag. Tom Murphy commented that I was a real toff last week with my ironed shirt, and you could see yourself. in me shoes."

"If you think I am going to wash and cook for you, Baldi, you are mistaken. There's enough work here already. Wouldn't you think of getting a wife? There must surely be some poor girl out there who would have you."

"Not at all, Alice, sure a wife would break you. With all the fancy notions they have nowadays, I'd be broke in no time. Not that there's not plenty of them out there who would be glad to get into Ballinamona, but I'm too clever for them. They may look in, but they won't look out."

Alice raised her eyes to heaven. Not much change there, she thought. He'd hardly spend Christmas if he could help it, holding on to it so one of Mick's lads can spend it when he's gone.

A week later, after the six o'clock news, Alice took the opportunity to share her anxieties withWilson.

"I've been thinking, Wilson, I won't stay if Baldi comes back. He gave myself and Ruby a terrible time when we were young and you remember when father and mother were ill he never once sat up with them, leaving myself and yourself to do all the night nursing. He thinks of nobody but himself and I won't skivvy for him."

"Don't you worry, Alice, this is just a notion. He'll change his mind. That's not the first time he talked of selling."

"No, Wilson, I've my mind made up. If he comes back, I'll go. I'll be sorry to leave you, but I'll go over to Ruby in Leeds. She says there are plenty of jobs for good workers and I am a quick learner.'

"I can't stop you, girl, but I'd be mighty sorry to see you go."

"I see the place up for sale on the paper, Baldi," said Wilson two weeks later as he read the Nationalist. "You'll get a tidy sum for it now. Prices are on the way up and that place is well watered and fenced."

"I hope so. there's a lot of interest .It's better be rid of it. Farming is a fool's game, too much work for too little money. There's plenty of room for me here, and sure it will give Alice something to do looking after the two of us. I have to hand it to her, she's a great housekeeper. Mick Eardley missed out."

"Don't be too sure of that, Baldi. She mentioned to me that she might go over to Ruby."

"She won't do that. She was never anywhere and not trained for anything. Who'd have her now? No, this is where she'll stay, mark my words."

The nights were beginning to close in. Wilson stood in the yard. The Tilly lamp had just been lit in the kitchen He watched the bats one by one leave their roost from the eave gutters by the end of the house. One by one, they darted out into the dark, delaying slightly, he thought, to give the next group time to arrange themselves for flight. The kitchen curtains had not yet been pulled and he could see Alice putting down the fire for the night, and putting out the cocoa mugs on the table for the last time. Tomorrow she would be gone. He couldn't bear to think what would become of her and of him. He had tried to get her to change her mind, but she was adamant.

"I'll take the bicycle as far as the cross roads," she said to Wilson as she finished dragging the brown leather suitcase down the stairs later that night. "You can get himself to collect it later."

Wilson turned to face the fire, took the pipe from his mouth, cleared his throat and spat into the fire. Turning around awkwardly, he muttered: "I suppose it's too late to ask you to change your mind."

"It is Wilson, I'm going to take my chances. I am a good worker and a good housekeeper and I'm sure there is many a one who will be glad of my services and, who knows, I may even get a husband and rear a family. Ruby will meet me in Leeds There's no hope in this place and I can't put up with Baldi's cutting remarks any more."

Next morning Alice took the brass key from the hook at the end of the dresser. She made her way to the bicycle shed by the red iron gate. There was a time when there was more than one bicycle there, but now the only one was Alice's. Fumbling with the key she put it in the lock and opened the door. The dry, musty smell invaded her nostrils and she began to sneeze. The brown suitcase wobbled on the carrier as she turned the bicycle for the car road.

Wilson stood by the pump pulling on his pipe. His eyes filled with tears. "Alice, there's always a home for you here if it doesn't work out, but I won't stand in your way. God speed you, girl." He watched her as she went across the car-road and then he turned in to the empty kitchen.

"Are you happy, now," he said to Baldi as he finished his breakfast. "You had to make a mess of things. We were happy here until you poked your nose in. Mind you, I won't be catering for you."

Wilson took his seat by the fire and pulled on his pipe, the waves of smoke curling up to the high ceiling. He looked at the clock on the dresser and then at Baldi as he drained the last drop of tea from the blue-rimmed mug.

"Better be going down to collect that bike, Baldi. The Dublin bus will be gone by now and we don't want some young lad being the better of Alice's bike."

"God send her good luck," he muttered as he took another pull of the pipe and stared at the reddening fire.

The Shoemaker's Secret

By Clare McAfee,
Ballycastle, Co. Antrim

We knew Granda said many prayers for all of us but only one for himself. He didn't reveal what that special prayer was. It was one secret he never told

When w e were children, my mother used to take us in to see Granda John at work in his cobbler's shop in Castle Street. It was an old-fashioned place, even by nineteen-fifties standards. There was a wonderful, all-pervading smell of leather and the battered wooden counter was also a workbench. On the walls hung bundles of bootlaces resembling bunches of liquorice strips. The floor was always littered with scraps of hide like pieces of an extremely difficult jigsaw puzzle.

Granda John was, at that time, a mild-mannered man in his seventies. He always seemed pleased to see us and told us stories of the old days as he worked. He described how the farmers who came to the Hiring Fair in Ballycastle would bring their freshly-hired labourers up to his shop and pay him to fit their workers out with new leather boots so that they would have strong footwear for the coming year's toil.

He rarely spoke of his childhood, but he did tell a tale about the time when he had been sent to work on a farm. When a pig was slaughtered, the carcass had to be delivered to the pork store in Ballymoney, some seventeen miles away. None of the adults could be spared from gathering in the harvest so the farmer sent Granda John off driving a horse and cart with the dead pig in the back.

He was only ten years old, had never driven a horse before and didn't know the way to Ballymoney. However, the farmer told him that he would see other carts with dead pigs on board and he should simply follow them. He took this advice and completed his mission successfully. When my mother protested at the irresponsibility of the farmer who sent a child on such an errand, Granda replied calmly: "Things were different then, Jean."

My father's parents lived next to us in a semi-detached cottage. Once, when my father was cautiously attempting to open a bottle of our home-made ginger beer, the cork shot off with an explosion taking half the liquid with it. Amidst the ensuing excitement my five-year-old sister fell from the top of the stairs to the bottom. Within minutes, Granda John was in our house, having heard the commotion next door. He had only paused to arm himself with a couple of sugar lumps, his remedy for every childhood misfortune.

Sometimes my Granny would prefix a piece of local news with the words: "I'm not sure if this is true so don't be repeating it." Granda John would invariably reply: "Well, don't be telling me for you know I can't keep a secret."

"There goes Saint Joseph," Granny would murmur affectionately when her husband crept upstairs each evening for she knew he went to his room to pray. We knew that he said many prayers for all of us, but only one for himself. He never revealed what this special prayer was. That was one secret he never told.

When I was twelve, Granny became ill. Her hospital treatment was unsuccessful and she was sent home. My mother nursed her until the end. I overheard Granda asking her anxiously: "Jean, what will I do if anything happens to Annie? We don't have the money to pay for her funeral."

He seemed reassured when she whispered: "Don't you worry about that, John. She has enough put by for both of you."

After Granny died in December, 1962, my mother started sitting with Granda in the evenings so he wouldn't be lonely, but he told her there was no need. "I know you mean well, Jean," he said, "but I have no company since Annie left."

Granda John spent Christmas with us. Then he got into a

routine and seemed to be coping. However, in February came the big snow of 1963 and that kept him indoors. My father worked for the roads' service in those days and, although our district was not in his jurisdiction, he cleared our road with the snowplough. Granda was pleased to be able to get out and about again.

I knew something was wrong when, a few days later, I came home from school to find our lunchtime dishes unwashed and the remains of a saucepan of rice pushed to the back of the range. Then Dad arrived and stated frankly: "Your Granda's dead. He went to bed last night and never woke up."

Later, I heard how mother had found him in a coma and sent for a doctor who had examined the patient and commented: "If I had to choose a type of death for myself this peaceful ending would be my choice."

Amongst his possessions they found his well-thumbed prayer book. Tucked inside its pages was the shoemaker's secret prayer for himself...his handwritten copy of the Prayer for a Happy Death. I'm sure Annie was waiting for him when his time came.

CHANGES

By Alex Lee Parsey,
Ballygawley, Co. Tyrone

Faced with the loss of his home, an old man looks back on his life

FRANK CORDINER knocked on the cottage door, opened it and stepped inside without an invitation. Joseph Mallen was sitting on the edge of his chair in front of the fire; his elbows resting on his knees. He was holding a mug of stewed tea. Frank stood in the doorway wondering how to attract the old man's attention without startling him. He didn't like this business. He jangled the loose change in his trouser pocket, but he knew Joseph was hard of hearing; he was playing for time. As he shifted his weight from hip to hip, Joseph became aware of his visitor and glanced over his shoulder.

"Frank, it's you. Tea in the pot if you want a drop," Joseph said, turning back to face the fire. Its flames burned blue and orange as they sizzled the sticky sap from a log. Frank placed his hand on Joseph's shoulder before sitting in the chair next to him. The teapot sat like a hen in a nest in the ashes on the hearth. Flames had scorched its surface black, and the steam that leaked from its spout mingled with the wood-smoke to blend into a curious smell of singed tea-leaves.

"I'll not have tea," answered Frank. He looked at Joseph's rheumy knuckles bent around the mug. They were so different to his own, smooth, lightly-freckled hands.

"What's your business, Frank," the old man asked. His pale blue eyes were dulled with the on-set of cataracts, yet the fire-light found a glint in them that hinted at an inner shrewdness. He knew Frank's visit was more than just a neighbourly call. Frank avoided the old man's stare by inspecting his own shoes;

brown brogues with thick stitching that gripped the hide in endless swirls.

"I just thought I'd call in. See how things are with you, Joseph." A light back-draft from the chimney pushed a plume of creamy smoke into the room; it crept over the mantle-piece and up the chimney breast wall to join the yellowed circle on the ceiling. They both watched it hover in the air like a ghost until it disappeared leaving only its smoky odour.

"I'm the same as usual," Joseph answered, still looking into Frank's face trying to figure out why he was here. Frank kept his eye-lids lowered; the lashes were amber coloured in the fire-light. He pressed the toes of his shoes together like a guilty child. Joseph watched him shift in the chair to cross one leg over the other; the wood creaked with his discomfort.

"You know Uncle Ignatius passed away last month," he finally said.

"I do. God rest his soul." Joseph sat back in his seat now to await the reason for Frank's visit.

"Well, he left this place to me, Joseph. And well...It's just that...well Joseph..."

"Are you looking to up the rent, Frank?"

"No, no, Joseph. Your family have been here for two generations. Not at all," Frank feigned shock; they both stared into the fire. The wind was gathering pace outside. It slapped the ivy against the window pane and shook the leaves on the big chestnut tree, whose branches, when bent, tapped the red tin roof of the house.

"So, what's your problem, Frank," Joseph asked.

"It's just that up until last year, Joseph, this place and the acre and a half with it, well it wouldn't have made much, but the way the price of land and property in Northern Ireland is now. Well, it's catching up with the mainland."

"What are you telling me, Frank?" Joseph held his breath inside, afraid that the sound of his own breathing would make him miss what Frank was going to say.

"It's 2006, Joseph. This place, on the open market could make a quarter of a million." Frank was excited suddenly at the thought of it. "Imagine that, Joseph! A quarter of a million pounds! Can you believe that?"

Joseph reached up to the mantle-piece to lift down his pipe. He stared at the empty bowl.

"What do you think, Joseph," Frank asked, calming himself; trying to judge the old man's mood.

"What do I think? I think where the bloody hell do you expect me to go? That's what I think." Joseph lifted the tobacco pouch from the side of his chair and began pressing some flakes into the pipe's bowl, the tobacco's freshness made it springy under his thumb.

"Don't you worry about that, Joseph. I'll get you a place. You won't have to leave the townland and I'll make sure it's a decent rent," Frank was looking at Joseph now, willing him to be as enthusiastic about the plan as he was. Both men fell silent. Frank's excitement diminished as Joseph's panic grew.

"This is my home, Frank. I was born in this house."

"I know, I know. I don't want to do this, Joseph. But I might never get a chance like this again. Please, Joseph, try to understand!"

"Who would want to live in this aul' place? Sure it's crumbling. There is only me that knows it and would want to live in it," Joseph said.

"Well, I would be knocking this place down and putting up a bungalow before I would be selling it," Frank said.

"Knocking it down! Knocking it down! You'll be knocking nothing, Frank Cordiner. You'll take yourself out of it!" Joseph's neck and face purpled in rage. He gripped the arm of his chair with one hand and threw down his pipe with the other onto the floor. Frank tried to calm him.

"Now, Joseph, there's no call for that. I will give you ample time to get yourself sorted. It's not like I'm putting you out on the street." Joseph wasn't listening. He was on his feet with his fists clenched by his sides, rage trembling through him.

"You'll get out of this house! I still pay the rent and you'll not come in here with your threats." Joseph stood as straight as his seventy-eight-year-old frame would allow him. As Frank stood to leave, both men faced each other. Joseph's feet welded themselves to the floor in stubbornness while Frank moved sideways across the room. He paused in the doorway to say, "Joseph, this isn't personal. You understand that?" Joseph didn't move except to clench his jaw. The sound of Frank's car engine leaving the yard gradually weakened Joseph's muscles. He sat down heavily into his chair, trembling with anger and shock.

The wind had grown stronger and lashed rain onto the roof. He had always been comforted by the sound of the cold raindrops bouncing off the corrugated tin, but now they sounded more like a threat. The sky was a winter sky, grey and damp.

He wasn't sure how long he had been sitting in the chair, but the fire had almost died away. He placed a couple of sticks onto what was left of the embers and watched them spark and slowly kindle. It was past the time for closing the goat into her shed. She would wonder where he was, he thought, as he shovelled a few pieces of coal onto the fire. Joseph pulled on his coat and cap to go outside.

Dilly was standing inside the doorway of the shed. Her strange rectangular eyes were searching his for the reason why he was so late. He never left her out till this time normally. He touched her head, her white coat grey now in the dusk.

"It's alright girl. We're late the night." He went inside to sit on a bale of straw. She followed him and climbed up to sit beside him on the rough bale. When he looked into her eyes they changed shape in the dimming light. They became oval and soulful. She looked almost ancient; a mythical creature with a secret understanding.

"Ah, Dilly, my wee girl. You can't sit on my knee now like when you were on the bottle." She leaned up against him, the heat from her body warmed his and his, in turn, warmed hers. Her horns were hard against his thigh, but he didn't mind. Fat tears splashed onto his lap; he could feel them cool in the night air and chill his legs. Dilly didn't move. Her breathing deepened as she slept. He could see her bottom teeth as sleep slackened her jaw. He wondered what would become of them both.

Joseph held the lit match to the wick of the oil lamp. The fire was red and glowing, making shadows on the white-washed walls; the light from the lamp diminished them. A young boy stared from a small wooden picture frame next to the clock on the mantle.

Joseph lifted his pipe from where he had thrown it earlier. The tobacco hadn't spilled from it. He held it in his teeth and sucked it into life from a lit taper. He thought about the child, the image half-hidden behind the pipe smoke. As it cleared, he gazed at his son, a smiling twelve-year-old boy wearing a shirt and tie and a hand-knitted V-neck sweater.

He remembered his laughter, his dimpled cheeks and his straight brown hair all slicked back by his mother's fussing. He remembered his coughing; his pale damp face; his sunken eyes and his final rasping breath. He remembered too the sound that Agnes had made as she clung to the lifeless child. A soul-shattering wail that he hadn't believed any human being could utter; a sound that had almost stopped his heart from beating.

The years had passed slowly after Thomas had gone. He had taken their joy with him to his grave. Agnes grew quiet. She worked hard; harder than was needed. It was as though she was afraid that if she slowed down, her pain would catch up with her and drown her in sorrow.

Joseph pulled the pipe smoke into his chest, it calmed him; the slight burning sensation on his tongue curbed his appetite. He hadn't eaten since breakfast and had forgotten to make dinner. Frank Cordiner's news had disrupted his perception of time. It was almost midnight and he hadn't even drawn the curtains.

He thought of Dilly curled up on the bale of straw asleep. He thought of the first time he had seen her, a leggy white hornless goat crying in the farmers' mart; lost and alone in a make-shift pen. Her cries touched him. They made him want to take her home.

The gruffness of the farmer who was selling her made him want her even more. They bartered and he paid twenty-five pounds for the eight-week-old Shaneen. He had lifted her into his arms, carried her to a feed stall and bought her a feeding bottle and powered milk. He fed her five times a day on his lap with her wrapped in a woollen blanket. Each time she drained the last of the milk, she instantly fell asleep. He had laid her on the chair next to the fire and watched her pink nostrils flare and contract as she breathed.

That was seventeen years ago and she had grown into a strong, solid goat with a chest muscle as firm as bone. The following year Agnes had died. It was a sudden death. There were no warnings, no doctors, just an up-turned peg basket and Agnes clutching the fence post as she slipped away. The hospital said she had had a stroke, but he knew better. She had died from a broken heart. It was too much losing Thomas. He had already said goodbye to her the day they had buried their son.

It had just been him and Dilly from then on. She followed him everywhere, her curiosity continually surprised him. She knew things; odd things. Like what room in the house he was in. No matter what window in the house he looked out from she was standing in the enclosure gazing at him. When he felt low, she would sit quietly beside him looking into his face as if she was reading his mind; his very soul even.

On warm summer days, when he lay in the field, she would lie with him, her head and legs across his chest until she got bored. Then she would push him with her head to make him get up so they could walk to another part of the field for her to nibble at the yellow gorse flowers in the hedge. When she had finished she would rise up on her hind legs and pretend to butt him, her head all to the one side until she dropped back down to all-fours to run and leap into the air and execute a perfect flip like an acrobat.

When she tired she would delicately sip clear well-water from her bucket and slide her lips back over her teeth, giving her the appearance of making a manic grin. It always made him laugh and he would tell her what a lovely girl she was. Sometimes, she grew restless and would find a way out through the wire fence. He would turn to see her standing next to him in the kitchen, watching him, waiting.

Dawn was breaking across the sky in the distance. Joseph

hadn't moved from his chair all night. The fire had died away hours ago, leaving a dusty pile of grey ash. There was still a faint hint of heat captured in the hearth's stone; a memory of what had been.

As Joseph stood outside, the birds hadn't begun their day and the last of the night's silence still hung in the damp air. The joints in his hips felt stiff; they hadn't got used to their change of position. Each step made his bones ache as he limped to the goat shed. As he slid back the bolt to open the door, he could see Dilly lying on the straw. He sat beside her, resting his hand on her back. She was still, under his palm. Joseph lifted her head to rest it on his lap. He watched the day break as Dilly pushed out her tongue to taste the morning air, and Joseph's chin sank into his chest as he slipped into sleep.

COMING HOME

BY MARY ANGLAND,
Kanturk, Co. Cork

It was one thing to come back for a few weeks in the summer, but living there permanently was different. Peter thought he had made a big mistake

PETER O'NEILL paced up and down the small neat kitchen of Fuchsia Cottage. When he had re-arranged the curtains for what must have been the tenth time, Teresa, his sister, couldn't stay silent any longer.

"For heaven's sake, man," she'd scolded, "will you sit down for a minute and stop foostering?" But her tone was affectionate as she guided him to the back door of the cottage. "Look, go out and have a walk around the garden," she ordered, "it twill relax you, if nothing else." The look he gave her was both apologetic and grateful and, giving his arm a small squeeze, she watched with a fond smile as he disappeared down the garden path.

Had he been this nervous the first time? Peter didn't remember, it was a long time ago. Stretching back on the red garden seat, he let the soft rustling of the trees and the heat of the sun on his face, gradually soothe him.

At sixty-eight, Peter O Neill was still a fine looking man. Tall and thin, with his silver hair combed back neatly, he could well have passed for a man twenty years younger. He had only returned home to the small village of Curramore the previous year after spending most of his adult life in England. With barely a penny to his name, he had left home, like so many others, in the 1950s and arrived in Manchester where a former neighbour had got him a start in the building trade.

Those first few years were tough and there was more than one occasion when loneliness had almost forced him to pack it all in and return home on the first boat out of Liverpool. But he was stubborn and had his pride. He thought of coming back to the village and to the small cottage where his father and mother could barely make ends meet as it was, but he gritted his teeth and got on with it.

Every few weeks, he'd send a few bob home with a short letter, deliberately upbeat, telling them what a great place Manchester was and how much money a fella could make there if he was willing to work hard and stay out of the pubs. That last bit was true enough. There was plenty of work and more money than he'd ever seen in his life. But the pubs were a curse. He'd seen so many young men, lonely and lost, take to the drink so that they could face each day in the large, teeming city where they knew no one.

He was determined to avoid being sucked into that so he worked hard and long, and every summer, until first his mother, and, a few years later, his father, had passed away, he'd headed back to Ireland for a few weeks, catching up with family and gossip. After they died, home wasn't the same and he went less often, once every two or three years. He found, too, that most of the lads he grew up with had themselves taken the boat to England, and he was more likely to meet them on the building sites around Manchester and Birmingham than he was in the small village at home.

As the years passed, he grew more at home in England, and then he met Eileen at a dance in the Irish Club in Manchester. She was from Mayo and had been in England almost five years working as a maid with a wealthy family in the affluent suburb of Sneinton. They'd clicked straight away and were married three years later, settling down in a small terraced house just outside Manchester, where'd they'd lived for the rest of their married life.

They'd had no family, much to their regret, but they didn't allow what couldn't be to dominate their lives. Cliché and all as it was, they had each other and they were

89

happy. As the years passed, they'd bought their house from the corporation and enjoyed themselves a bit now that they weren't watching the pennies. They'd joined the bowling club, went hill- walking and, every so often, they'd go back to visit the relations in Mayo and Curramore. They'd even gone to Spain a few times. Peter hadn't liked it much. He preferred being at home, putting his feet up by his own fireside to being roasted alive in Spain. Thank God, Eileen never minded. She'd laughed at him, affectionately calling him her old stick-in-the-mud.

Then, two months after he retired, came the dreadful shock of Eileen's death. There she was, sitting opposite him at breakfast one minute, talking and drinking a cup of tea and the next, she'd fallen sideways and was gone, just like that. A massive heart attack, the doctor said. There was nothing anyone could have done.

In the beginning, Peter had been too heart-broken and shocked to do anything for weeks, except wander around the house in a daze. Then he'd forced himself out to meet friends, but it simply wasn't the same, not without Eileen. He went back to Ireland for a holiday three years after she died, saw the small cottage for sale in the village and decided, on a whim that he couldn't still explain, to make a complete break and return home.

In Peter's young days, the cottage had belonged to Master O'Boyle, the schoolteacher. The house was spotless and big enough for his needs now that he was alone, but it was the garden he fell in love with. There were neatly trimmed hedges bordered by colourful flowerbeds and apple trees and a little pond in the middle with a red garden seat beside it. The day he saw it, the sunlight danced lazily through the branches of the trees overlooking the garden and he felt an immediate pull. So, on impulse, he bought it and, within three months, he sold up everything in England, and moved in, lock, stock and barrel to Fuchsia Cottage.

It had taken him a while to settle. It was one thing to come back for a few weeks in the summer, but living there permanently was different. At first, he hardly knew what to do with himself and thought he'd made a dreadful mistake.

Many of the villagers were newcomers, busy young people, working in the nearby town. He'd persevered and, gradually, got chatting to people over a pint in the local or buying his messages in the local Quik Pick. He'd joined the Senior Citizens' Club and the Gardening Circle and made friends there, too.

The Senior Citizens' Club was very active and had a busy social schedule, organising trips to such places as Bunratty Castle and Croke Park. They'd even visited Dail Eireann and Aras an Uachtarain where they met the President. Once or twice a month, in his small car, he visited his younger sister, Teresa, who lived only an hour or so from Curramore. With the clubs and the gardening, he was kept busy and, in the twelve months since he'd settled there, had become part of the fabric of village life.

At night in the silence of the cottage, Peter admitted that despite his friends and his outings and his garden, he was still lonely. Lonely for companionship and someone to talk to, someone with whom he could share his thoughts and have a bit of a laugh with - like he'd done with Eileen.

Well, that only happened once in a lifetime, he thought, and gave himself a mental shake. "For goodness sake, man, stop feeling sorry for yourself," he'd admonished himself. "Count your blessings, there's many a man that would be happy to step into your shoes." So he counted his blessings and when, at times, he felt an ache of loneliness stealing over him, he ignored it and got on with his life.

"That was fascinating." The voice had a soft Northern burr and Peter turned to find himself facing a well-dressed woman in her sixties, a woman he'd never seen before. She had bright blue eyes and was smiling at him. They'd just been listening to a talk by a well-known landscape gardener, Joe Sheridan - a talk Peter had been looking forward to enthusiastically and he hadn't been disappointed. The man had been inspirational and had so fired Peter up that he now forgot his customary shyness in front of women.

"Wonderful," he agreed enthusiastically, "I can't wait to try out a few of those ideas of his for shady corners."

"I can't either," the stranger confessed. "Such simple ideas too, that's the beauty of it."

They chatted for a few minutes and then Peter held out his hand.

"Peter O'Neill," he said.

"Muriel O'Reilly," the woman took his outstretched hand.

"Look," Peter said, looking around and noticing that people were beginning to make their way to the kitchen where refreshments were being served, "maybe, if you're not hurrying away, we could grab a cup of tea and some cake?"

"Why not," Muriel agreed.

In an unusual show of gallantry for the shy Peter, he held out his arm which Muriel took laughingly. That night they'd talked for what seemed like hours. Peter hadn't realised what a huge gap Eileen's death had left in his life. He'd spoken more, he reckoned later, in those couple of hours, than he'd done for the previous six months.

Muriel was a widow, she'd told him, and originally from Holywood, in County Down. She was in Curramore visiting her sister, Esther, who was married a mile or so outside the village. Peter knew her sister by sight, but hadn't ever had the opportunity to speak to her or her husband.

Muriel, herself, had married a Wexford man and settled down in Gorey, her husband Bill's home town, where they'd lived for almost forty years until Bill's death two years before. She told him about her two grown-up children: Sean, working in Brussels, and Marie, in London. With both children away, Muriel had found herself lonely and unsettled after Bill's death.

"You feel like a spare part, rattling round the kitchen," she'd confessed to Peter, who agreed whole-heartedly. He and Eileen hadn't been blessed with children, he'd told Muriel, a hint of regret in his voice when Muriel told him of how close she and her children were and of their frequent visits home. Muriel was so easy to talk to it was with a shock that Peter realisedmost of the people had left for home and Tom, the caretaker of the hall where the Gardening Circle held their talks, was waiting to lock up and go home.

Well, after meeting Muriel, he'd had a new lease of life. They'd begun spending more and more time together. No longer was the cottage a lonely place, it echoed with the sound of chatter and laughter. Muriel, like Eileen was easy to be around and they shared so many interests, including gardening and walking – they even liked the same type of music and books. When Peter asked Muriel to marry him and she accepted, nobody in the village, except perhaps Peter himself, was surprised.

Peter brought himself back to the present. Goodness, had he actually dozed off? To his surprise, he no longer felt nervous and when he rose from the seat, it was with a sense of purpose and confidence. In less than an hour, in front of family and friends at the small village church, he and Muriel would be married. As he hurried up the path, eager now for the ceremony to begin, he imagined he felt the spirit of Eileen smiling down at him approvingly.

THE PLANK

BY SHEELAGH MOONEY,
Hazelmere, Co. Kildare

*I could scarcely believe my mother was sending me on such a
dangerous mission, but she was serious and there was nothing for it
but to arm myself with a stick and set off*

A NARROW PLANK separated our house from our farm
next door. The plank spanned a good ten feet width and
had a drop of some six feet down to a rather muddy,
nettle-lined ditch. This piece of wood provided the shortcut to
the farm.

There was, of course, access by road, but since the road
was out of bounds to us younger users, everyday we literally
walked the plank. We would run over and back several times
a day to visit my father while he worked and the menagerie of
animals that lived on the other side of the plank.

I was always a bit wary of the crossing, for, to a small child,
the drop must have appeared as deep as the Niagara Falls. I
must have been little more than four years old when I was
called up for my first important duty on the other side of the
plank. My father was away at a mart and my mother was busy
in the kitchen whipping up a feast of flans and sandwiches for a
family gathering that night. I was availing of a rare opportunity
to play with my brother's matchbox cars and farm set on the
mat by the fire nearby, while he was safely out of the way at
school.

Suddenly from the farm could be heard the raucous sound
of hens squawking and cackling. My mother declared that
perhaps there might be a fox in the farmyard and asked me
to run across the plank to scare it off. I stared at her open-

mouthed. I had never seen a fox in the flesh and had no desire to. My knowledge of foxes came from Ladybird books in which little red hens met their untimely end in the jaws of some wily fox. And then, of course, there was Little Red Riding Hood and the wolf - were foxes anything more than wolves kitted out in red clothing?

I could scarcely believe that my normally cautious mother was sending me on such a dangerous mission. I stared at her face and, seeing no trace of humour there, I realised she was serious. There was nothing for it but to arm myself with a stick and set off.

I found a suitable weapon in the form of an ash plant, my father normally used for rounding up cattle, aiming the odd tap on an adventurous rump, and headed towards the plank. My heart was beating so loudly I feared that fox would hear me coming and lie in wait for me.

I tiptoed across the plank, crept along the back of the hay barn, through the cowshed and finally peeped out from the shed door. Mother was right, the fox was circling the terrified cackling hens looking for suitable prey. I, however, was frankly unprepared for the beauty of my opponent. When she fixed her tawny eyes on me I was transfixed by the rich red coat and the fine chiselled face. She was nothing like the wolf I imagined.

I watched in utter fascination as she boldly met my eye, obviously getting the measure of her opponent. Then, keeping one eye on me, she fearlessly reached over and swept up one of the squawking hens and sauntered towards the field gate, disappearing while I stood motionless, stick raised, in the doorway to the now empty yard. Only a trail of red feathers across the cobblestones leading to the field accounted for the missing hen.

I ran back across the plank to tell my Mother about the beautiful creature that I had just encountered and the demise of the red hen, happily unaware that I had just learned a valuable lesson that sometimes beautiful creatures can literally get away with murder in this world.

FOR A GOOD HOUR I HAVE BEEN SINGING LAYS

BY PATRICIA CARR,
Fanad, Co. Donegal

A young musician describes halcyon days when it seemed that prosperity would never end, and he is shocked when clouds begin to appear on the horizon, bringing warnings of dark days ahead

"SINGING, FOR A LIVING, talk sense, son," my father said, when I announced that I intended to quit school early and take up a career in music.

"Singing - huh, an out-of-tune version of "Galway Bay" as you're passing the pub on the evening of a fair day," my mother replied.

"You'll go to the Tech and learn a trade - something solid that you can always fall back on."

Those were the days when you didn't say "no" to your father!

His reaction knocked me back a bit. There was a strong musical tradition in our family. My father was often called upon to play at dances, some up to twenty miles away. A last-minute message might be delivered to the Post Office, asking if he could come that very evening. He was always delighted to be asked. I was his "roadie" during school holidays. I made the odd appearance with the latest toe-tapping addition to my repertoire.

"Good man, but you didn't lick that off a stone."

"Give that lad of yours a few more years, Mickie, Cashel will not hold him."

Nor did they complain when my old accordion, wheezing and belching as I rehearsed some new tune, kept them awake into the small hours. While they encouraged my interest, they were adamant that music as a sole means of earning a living was a flimsy prospect.

There were few bands as such in my young days. Practically every townland boasted of having a musician. Most houses had some type of musical instrument. Travelling musicians added a touch of variety when they chanced to pass the way. There was little monetary reward. Any man who could draw a bow was a fiddler. Musicians took turns, providing a colourful medley of tunes, old and new.

"No, you are not going to the dance tonight," was mother's reply to my request.

"Our bargain was that you keep up your school work during school time."

Father's absence was my opportunity. Rarely was he home on a Sunday night. My brother, Ben, and I helped each other out of the bedroom window. We would drop noiselessly onto the fuchsia hedge behind the house, make our way across the meadow and there before us were the gleaming lights of the Denver Ballroom. The delights of those stolen moments of musical bliss will never be forgotten. We made a stealthy return, sometimes in the gathering dawn. Whether or not mother suspected, I never found out.

In keeping with their wishes, I enrolled for three years at the Vocational School, or the "Tech" as it was then known. There were no course choices. The curriculum was curtailed and offered little scope for talent development. Carpentry was the flagship training on offer. Beaming with delight, I presented my mother with the Christmas Crib I had turned out in class that year.

"P.J., I knew you were gifted with your hands. That's the most beautiful crib I have ever had," she gasped in delight.

Her enthusiasm was more than likely a ruse to encourage me in what she saw as the foundation for a sensible future.

There was little emphasis on the academic at the Tech. There was the odd essay, which I would hastily copy from my friend, John. After making what I thought were requisite changes to his script, I would pass it off as my own work. If my teacher had his doubts, he kept them to himself. The ability to write a letter home when we emigrated was the extent of his ambitions for us, gifted or not.

The highlight of my year was the ceili held just before the holidays. With my hair sleeked with Brylcreem, my winkle-pickers polished to a fine point, I eagerly slung my melodeon over my back and waited for my chance to shine. I belted out jigs, reels and waltzes effortlessly. I could almost feel the torrent ofheated female admiration rise to the ceiling, drift towards me and envelope me in its glow. I basked in the glory, short- lived as it turned out to be.

The three years had run their course. My Group Cert results were a fair reflection of my ability as a carpenter. I acquired an apprenticeship with my uncle Mike.

"What time do you call this?" he would roar from a distance.

"Your jacket is on a shaky peg, coming in any old time, and yawning for most of the forenoon. I suppose you are not long home. Were you in bed at all, or are you after dropping the melodeon and coming straight here?" Many was the day I got the same extended tongue-lashing .

Though he seemed harsh at the time, I realised later that the sense of work ethic which he instilled in me would stand me in good stead later on.

Cashel could no longer hold me. Buoyed up by the hope of enhancing my musical career and the prospect of promotion in my day job, I took the Derry boat. I was mesmerised for my first few days in London. I sought out the Irish clubs, which were numerous.

The most noted of these was the Galtymore on Cricklewood, Broadway. Looking from the upstairs balcony, I felt I was back in Ireland. Here was the thirty-third county transplanted into North London. I could not help but notice how the women congregated on one side, men on the other, a hangover from the old Irish dancehalls. From my vantage point, I viewed the talent, but could not summon up enough courage to make a move in its direction.

Instead, I followed a small stairway to the left. It led to another door. When I entered the room, I was almost blasted off my feet....

Apart from the main ballroom, there was a totally separate area devoted to ceili music and dance. I dallied around, striking up a conversation with the box player as he packed up his gear.

"Are you not from Abbeyshrule?" I enquired

"I am indeed, did I not see you somewhere before?"

"Casey's the name, P.J. Casey. I'm from Cashel in Donegal," I answered

"I heard you play at the Old Denver a few years ago. What are you at now in London," he asked.

"The ould building sites. I'm a qualified chippie."

"Would you give us a hand out in the band if we are stuck for a singer or box-player some night?"

"No bother at all. Here's the address and phone number."

My foot was on the first rung of the entertainment ladder.

Many was the evening I sought a long rest after having been on the building site since 5 a.m. No sooner had I settled than a phone call would summon me to the bandstand at short notice. I became a regular fixture in the Galty, with special requests most nights for my rendering of the "Old Bog Road."

Keeping up with two occupations was a challenge for me. Were it not for my parents' advice branded on my brain, I might have had the courage to chuck the building job. They were getting on and the last thing I wanted was to disappoint them in their declining years. I went home on holiday.

"'Tis tanned and fit you are looking, son. That healthy outside work must suit you,." was my father's greeting.

"Sure you would get plenty work at home now in your trade." The hope in his voice left me in no doubt but that there was nothing more he wanted than my return for good.

Every year it seemed to me that Ireland was turning a corner, economically and socially. There was free secondary education for all. Talents were identified and students were encouraged to make the most of them. Employment was being created, new buildings were being developed, jobs were available and, most encouraging of all, the tide of emigration had turned.

My father's words have echoed in my mind ever since. He was proved right many times in the years that followed. I was set up, before I had a chance to draw my breath, as foreman carpenter on a scheme where two hundred and fifty houses were being built and another one hundred were in the pipeline. Farmers were availing of generous subsidies, through the intervention of the Common Market, and prices for their produce were buoyant.

This new-found prosperity spilled over into the world of leisure and entertainment. The humble dance-hall mineral bar, with its condensation soaked walls, was no match for the plush new lounges being refurbished in licensed premises up and down the country. The pub became the centre of social life. It was used as the venue for dances, concerts, music nights and even Pioneer quizzes. The guest musician would set up and sing a few opening songs. It was then time to bring on the local talent.

"Special request now for Mickey to oblige the company."

"Come on Mickey," one could hear through enthusiastic applause.

"No, no, my throat is bad."

"Ah, Mickey, come on, give us the Dark Island."

Mickey and several others like him loved the idea of taking the stage. The quality of the singing didn't seem to matter at all. They kept the craic going. Young and old looked forward to the pub music, and seats in the lounges were all taken by 9 p.m. A new breed of musician traversed the Irish venues – the one-man band.

This, of course, was right into my barrow. Without much thought, I packed in my day job, bought a Transit van and became a full-time musician. At the height of summer, I would leave home as the starlings were going to bed, getting back as the lark was shaking the dew off her wings to greet the dawn. My name appeared in every local paper weekly, and I became a minor celebrity. By now, I was earning enough from the singing alone to provide a decent home for myself, my young wife and our infant son. There was also a never-ending number of carpentry jobs that needed doing. I took on what I could manage and this allowed me the extra money for an exotic foreign holiday every year.

Those were the halcyon days. I thought this prosperity would never end, at least not for my time. But clouds began to form and gather momentum. The grand old characters who had so much to offer in terms of repartee and song were falling victim to the grim reaper. For each one of them who left us, the company was all the poorer. A younger generation weaned on television could not replace the vacancies. Television, having killed conversation in the home, was now set to do the same in the pub.

The increase in alcohol prices dampened enthusiasm for the "round" system, thus encouraging people to drink individually. It became more difficultfor the rural motorist to escape the dragnet of the breathalyser patrols.

The building trade and the country's economy generally were crumbling. Many took advantage of the cut-price alcohol in supermarkets to have a quiet drink at home. A modern slogan summed up the situation: "Staying in is the new going out."

It's New Year's Eve. Finding the venue provides my first hassle. Then I drive slowly, conscious of the possibility of black ice. I get there and hump my gear through the bar area. The few stragglers at the counter eye me like I am an interesting inanimate object. Should I start, or dare I compete with the television that no one in particular is watching?

"A lesson too late for the learning" is my opening set as the hum of conversation rises an octave. An awkward pause greets the end of the first set, with rationed applause. I am thick -skinned by now, a veteran of the high stool. Gradually, the customers, draining their glasses, filter out through the swing door.Few come in. I am feeling lonely up here.

For the past hour, I have been singing lays to an ever emptying space.

SMOG AND A MIDNIGHT FUNERAL

By Maura Flynn,
Westport, Co. Mayo

If I close my eyes, I can still see the coffin and the tail-lights of the hearse. It was a ghostly sight and we did not sleep that night

IN THE WINTER OF 1952, we heard on the radio that something called "smog" had hit London, bringing the city to a standstill. I was seven years old, young and carefree and wondering what Santa would bring me on Christmas Eve.

London, to me, was a place our relatives went to make a living and "smog" was a word I had never heard before. Yet soon its smutty black tentacles crept from that far-off city to our tiny west of Ireland village, bringing with it heartache and pain.

Our neighbours, Bridget and Tommy, had a daughter, Bridie, a nurse in London. Mother Heneghan, as she was affectionately known, came to our house every day and had a cup of tea with my mother - always calling out as she came in our ever-open door: "Is the tae boiled?"

On a winter's day, Mother Heneghan came, as usual, across the field separating our houses, but her greeting was not a happy one. I can still hear her calling out: "Bridie is dead! Bridie is dead!" I can still see the telegram in her hand. Bridie had been killed by a London bus as she crossed the street in the thick smog.

Death to us children was just a word and we were too young to understand its finality. Everyone in the village rallied round with food and help on the farm while they waited for Bridie's body to be brought home for burial. Her coffin came to Dublin by boat, and then by hearse to our local church. It was after midnight when it arrived in the village and stopped outside Bridie'shome for a few minutes. Due to the lateness of the hour we were not allowed to go to the church, but we watched from an upstairs window. If I close my eyes, I can still see the coffin in the back of the hearse surrounded by lights, and the tail-lights of the hearse fading in the distance as it made its way to the church. It was a ghostly sight and we did not sleep that night.

I often think of that midnight funeral and the way the London smog made its way into our young lives. Up to four thousand people were known to have died as a result of the smog. Cattle were asphyxiated in the fields and travel was disrupted for days. But for me, it will always be associated with that midnight funeral and the memory of Mother Heneghan running towards our house waving that telegram.

IN GRATEFUL APPRECIATION

BY MARIE O'HALLORAN,
Charleville, Co. Cork

When Eileen died, her relatives descended on the grand old eighteenth century house, marking out their spoils. Eileen left them to their plundering

MAURA TURNED the key and the large white Edwardian front door eased open. The silence echoed as she stepped into the black and white tiled hallway. "It's only me, Eileen." Her voice reverberated as she announced her arrival.

She nodded, as she did every morning, to the statue of the Child of Prague, on the stand in the hall. Maura passed by the numerous pictures hanging all over Eileen's house. They were of opening nights of shows she appeared in, or award ceremonies she had attended. Maura never tired of looking at them.

Eileen was awake, waiting for Maura in her bedroom. Maura Moore's little cottage was only five hundred yards from the entrance gates to Eileen Downey's grand house.

"Right, now let's get you up." Maura got no response. Not unusual, she thought, so she continued regardless.

Maura never knew what kind of mood Eileen would be in. Lately, she was cranky and frustrated. Having been active and fit, a former actor and dancer, Eileen now found it incredibly difficult relying on another to dress and bathe her. Eileen didn't like to let on, but she appreciated Maura and everything she did. She knew just how Eileen liked her eggs cooked. She knew the exact way to melt the butter so it would soak into her toast. Three-quarters of a teaspoon of sugar, not a spoon or half a spoon, in her tea, Maura never needed to be reminded.

"Would you like to put on your emerald green dress today?" Maura couldn't be certain, but she may have seen a trace of a smile on the old lady's face. She was sure Eileen's grip was more affectionate than dependent when she got her into her wheelchair. She knew that when Eileen was in this mood, the only way to cheer her up was to get her to put on one of her beautiful vintage dresses. The green one, being her favorite, made her feel regal. Maura knew it brought her back to happy, active, pre-stroke times.

When Eileen was dressed, Maura brought her to the reception room and asked her about the famous night she wore the dress. Eileen found her voice.

"I'll do my best to remember. Let me see..." It didn't take Eileen long to get into the flow of the tale.

Maura listened intently, while she worked, interested as if she were told the story for the first time.

Eileen didn't get many visitors, certainly none from her relatives. In fact, in the years that Maura worked for her she couldn't remember a single one calling. Not even a phone call to enquire of Eileen's wellbeing. Eileen had no children of her own, a reality she shared with Maura who was now forty-seven.

Weather permitting, Maura would take Eileen out to her huge garden as often as she could. Eileen's face would glow at the sight of the blooms. Bursts of pinks, reds, purples and yellows arranged with such precision that the result looked effortless.

The landscaping was tended to daily by her kind neighbour, William Hayes. William was a widower, in his early fifties. A quiet and polite gentleman, he would tip his cap as the ladies passed, before returning to the job at hand. He admired how Maura had such dedication to Eileen, modest about his own input. He had a gentle way of removing lifeless greenery from plants. In autumn, he would gather leaves fallen from the numerous trees lining Eileen's driveway, making it safer for Maura.

Over the years, Maura told Eileen stories about her parents, James and Mary. Maura was an only child. At twenty-five, she gave up her career as nurse in London, returning to Bantry to help her father care for Mary when she fell ill. Maura also left behind her fiancé, Sean.

James only lasted six weeks after Mary passed. Heart attack, they said, but Maura knew what it really was, a broken heart. Eileen never let on she saw tears welling up in Maura's eyes as she spoke of her parents and Sean. Sean never forgave her for moving home and they never spoke again.

"I worry about you in that cottage all alone," Eileen regularly said to her, and hoped that she would find a companion. Eileen didn't really want to share her, but knew that Maura had enough love to go round. One day she would let her know how she felt. Over time, Eileen noticed that Maura spoke less of Sean. Someone had put a spring in her step and a glint in her eye. She knew that Maura would tell her when she was ready, but Eileen had good instincts.

Maura didn't meet Eileen's niece or nephews until the following May. That was when they came home from England to bury her. She had a quiet, but insistent word with the undertaker; it was the only time she dared interfere. Maura knew that Eileen wanted to be buried in her emerald green dress, and Maura ensured that happened.

Her relatives didn't seem to care. They quickly descended on the grand old eighteenth century house, marking out their spoils. Maura was disgusted and left them to their plundering.

Maura was surprised when she received notification from the solicitor to attend the reading of Eileen's will at her house. She didn't want anything of Eileen's. Anyway, she thought, there won't be much left after her niece and nephews have finished.

Upon her arrival, Maura was greeted by George Torpey of Torpey and Finch, solicitors. Four weeks had gone by since Maura had been in Eileen's house. She missed her terribly and the pain of her passing stirred up in Maura's heart again.

She had spent the last few weeks crying, but managed to hold the tears back as she stepped into the hall. She nodded her greeting to the statue of the Child of Prague, as she had done daily for over eight years. She made her way into the living room.

She looked around in horror at the state of Eileen's home, it was all she could do to resist the urge to pick up a duster and polish. Pausing at the door, she tutted with disapproval.

"Eileen would be disgusted at the amount of dust on her mahogany furniture," she muttered. But as much as I care it's no longer my place to do anything, she thought. It saddened her.

She recognised Eileen's niece, Anne, and her two nephews, Damien and Patrick, from the funeral. They hadn't made much effort to speak to her that time and Maura got the distinct impression they only saw her as the hired help and no more. They never enquired of Eileen's last few years on this earth. They didn't seem to care that she passed away peacefully in her sleep after a wonderful day in her garden. She received a forced nod from all three as she took the seat at the end of the row beside William Hayes. He met Maura with a broad smile.

Once everyone was present the solicitor began.

Eileen left the house and most of its contents to Anne, Damien and Patrick. They didn't even have the decency to hide their triumph as Damien let out a quiet "yes!" and they all but high-fived each other. William and Maura kept their eyes fixed on Mr. Torpey, pretending not to notice their reaction, as he continued reading from Eileen's will.

"To Mr. William Hayes, thank you for tending to my landscaping needs for many years. You kept my gardens stately for me to enjoy. To you, I leave three thousand euro worth of prize bonds. I'm sure they will be lucky for you."

Anne shot William a dirty look, clearly put out that the hired help had benefited.

"Finally to Maura, I leave you my Child of Prague statue. I hope it will bring you good fortune, for the Child of Prague must surely hold many a secret."

The solicitor finished up his business. Maura and William walked out through the hall. Maura stopped to pick up her statue as she passed. She could hear Damien laughing behind her. William and Maura turned at the same time.

"Thank goodness that eyesore is gone. It was going to a car boot sale." He continued laughing.

Maura didn't reply.

"What will you do with the house," William enquired.

He didn't hesitate with his answer. "Sell it off to the highest bidder, take the money and get the hell out of here. We've instructed the solicitor to advertise it as soon as the paperwork is transferred. We should get over the million for it."Damien rubbed his hands together gleefully.

Maura and William glanced at each other. They ignored his exultant mood and left.

Anne, Damien and Patrick were taken aback when Eileen's house sold for well under the expected price. Having done the sums, they knew that with inheritance taxes, solicitors and auctioneers' fees they would be left with a lot less than they originally thought. They were even more astounded when the highest bidders were Maura Moore and William Hayes. They did little to hide the fact that they were furious.

"How could the hired help afford a house like this?" Anne exclaimed.

Once again, William tended to the gardens with the same love as he had done for years and Maura busied herself inside the house. They were getting everything ready. An important event was to take place. The marquee was set up in the garden. This was where their wedding reception would be held.

On the hall table of the beautiful stately home, in its rightful place, stood the statue of the Child of Prague. Tucked safely in the drawer underneath was a letter addressed to Maura from Eileen. It was found when Maura examined the Child of Prague to see indeed what secrets it held.

Dear Maura,

I never got the chance to express my gratitude to you properly for the way you cared for me in the autumn of my life. You were like the daughter I never had. You always went above and beyond your duty as a carer and never grumbled.

Please look at the back of this letter. Attached to it is a coin. It's a rare 1907 American coin. I had it appraised and its current value is over nine hundred and fifty thousand pounds sterling.

Peter Somerfield will be waiting for your call at Somerfield

Auction Houses. He already has a buyer. Don't forget to pop another coin in its place "to ensure the house is never without money."

I might have been getting on in years, but I saw how bright William's face would shine each time you passed. My garden had been immaculate, I suspect, with you in mind to impress. I hope you will be very happy together.

Make sure to tell him to contact the prize bond people, as soon as possible. In February, one of the prize bonds came out with winnings of five hundred thousand euro and another has ten thousand euro. Pretty lucky, don't you think?

I have informed my solicitor on all of the above. He is fully aware of my wishes so you have nothing to worry about. Have a good life and I will never forget your compassion and love.

Kindest Regards and affection,

Eileen.

RITE OF PASSAGE

By Martin Malone
Athy, Co. Kildare

*There were things he said that I could not respond to and, in the
end, we just let the silence sit there like an unwelcome guest that
wouldn't move on*

I USED TO WRITE a weekly feature of 1,600 words for a
provincial newspaper. Eddie Hobbs, Brian Keenan, Mary
McCartney, John Minihan, and other notables featured
week in, week out. But towards the end of my association
with the newspaper I asked my father if he would agree to be
interviewed. After expressing some reservations, he agreed to
tell his tale.

He was seventy-six and had survived throat cancer for
sixteen years. As a jump jockey, he had won the Power Gold
Cup and Jameson Gold Cup at Punchestown. He had been
foreman to the powerful Weld stable on the Curragh for almost
three decades, and, in all, he'd spent fifty-four years working
for the same horse-racing dynasty.

So, I wanted to write about his horse-racing days but, more
importantly, about his cancer, which we had never really
discussed in depth. I thought that what he had to say might give
encouragement to others who found themselves in a similar
situation.

I knew he wasn't well, had been losing weight and his words,
when his voice grew tired, were almost impossible to make out.
I would catch a word and try to conjure sense, very often did.
But there were things he said that I could not respond to, and
he would wait expectantly. In the end, we just let the silence
sit there like an unwelcome guest that wouldn't take a hint to

move on.

Monday, I placed my blue Olympus recorder on the armrest and invited him to talk away, prompting him with the occasional question. Everything went smoothly. The button popped and, in its popping, I always knew I had enough material to draft the story. I learned more about my father than I had bargained for- the places he had lived, the people he had known, family, a tapestry of informational bits and pieces, jigsaw tiles.

During the interview Jimmy, the photographer, rang me about a photo shoot he was doing for another interviewee of mine. He said he'd meet Dad at Weld's yard the next day and take the picture.

Tuesday, I arrived late on an overcast day and met with Jimmy and my father in the paddock. Jimmy had already taken the shots and showed these to me on his camera monitor: Dad had insisted on the photograph being taken alongside the statue of Blue Wind, the stable's first English classic winner.

After Jimmy left we walked around the yard. When I was a child he often brought me to Rosewell on the crossbar of his bike, to feed and water the horses, to check on a horse that was not well. The names of racehorses tripped across my mind: Tri-Star, Java Brown, Klairvimy, Boreen, Windy Glen…countless others. As we walked, my father spoke, but his voice was gone, the clarity blunted from his words.

Approaching the horse walker to show me a horse, he mentioned its name several times; but, frustratingly, I could only gather the word Ascot. Half an hour passed and then he came with me a little way across the paddock. We shook hands, I remember, and he said something lost to the air and smiled, and I knew, knowing him, it had to be witty and so smiled back.

Wednesday, the following day, my father died late afternoon in my mother's arms. A week later the newspaper published the interview and his photograph. Looking back on that sunny afternoon in the yard, piecing the memory together, the clues, I realised the name of the horse he had been talking about and I carried it in me for a long time, unable to bring myself to talk about it.

Eighteen months would pass before it somehow managed to slip out in a conversation after a literary workshop in Verona with my good friend, Anthony Glavin. The words were airborne before I realised - I felt the strain in my throat in their leaving, the weight abandoning my heart as I relayed the story and the name of the horse my father had so ardently wanted to talk to me about: "Rite of Passage...Rite of Passage."

LIVING THE DREAM

BY ROSE MCGRORY,
Lisburn, Co. Antrim

The fiftieth anniversary of the fateful voyage of the Titanic re-awakens old fears and brings back painful and disturbing memories

APRIL 1962. Through the open door I see my great-grandsons circling the flowerbeds, arms flapping like the wings of farmyard fowl. I try to guess if today's game involves flying or swimming as the older boy tumbles onto the grass.

"Help! Help! The ship's sinking. I'm drowning," he shrieks.

For the briefest moment, my heart flutters in my chest, and a chill runs through my bones. Nearby, my daughter Katie sits in a deck chair and shouts at them to keep the noise down.

"Quiet boys, Nana's trying to get a bit of peace."

April has crept in and a surprisingly strong sun has given nature an early nudge. The youngsters are besotted with all things nautical. The garden vibrates with their screams against the perpetual, pulsating rhythm of the Atlantic.

"I'm too old for this, I don't know what I was thinking of, bringing these two down on me own, madness it was." Katie gives up on the noise outside and joins me at the kitchen table. "Mary says now that she's got her little girl that'll be her lot, no more children."

I feel my daughter's pain, a mother worrying about her child. Two weeks after a long and difficult labour, my granddaughter was still not well enough to travel.

"I should maybe take a trip up to see the new arrival." I say this without any real conviction, lately I find myself slipping more and more into the past.

"It would do you the world of good to see your new great-grandchild and to get away from here. You didn't sleep too well last night, did you Mam?"She eyes me closely. "It's all that talk in the papers about the anniversary."

"Fifty years this week, so I suppose it's understandable everyone's going on about it."

"Strange how you never talked about it when Daddy was alive. It's only in the last few years I've learned about Nora and Jeremy and the Titanic." She looks thoughtful. Do you think Daddy minded that he wasn't your first choice?

"You know we seemed to have some sort of unspoken agreement over the years on avoiding the subject. If anything came on the wireless about the ship he would change the station."She reaches over to squeeze my hand before standing up.

"I am going to take these boys down to the shore, Mam, they'll sleep all the better for it tonight."

Moving to the door, I watch the three of them fade into the shoreline, their chatter engulfed by the waves. The new-found peace of the garden beckons and I ease myself into a deck chair. Lulled by the slow, somnolent, shifting of the Atlantic I am soon drifting back in time.

I think of the dream that started it all, and once more I find myself standing on the deck of that great ship as she ponderously pulls out of Cork harbour. There are people around me, shadowy, intangible figures. I cannot see their faces but I feel their presence. Queenstown fades into the distance until only St Colman's Cathedral is visible. The wind caresses my face.Overhead the gulls circle relentlessly. They follow the ship, hopeful of a crust or two from the multitude of humans pressing against the ship's railings. We pass a mantle of green fields spreading inland. The first whisperings of unease gather inside me, as the undulating Cork coastline gives way to the rugged cliffs of neighbouring County Kerry. In the background, the purple and blue of the McGillycuddys dominate the horizon.

We reach Ireland's most southerly point and the sky darkens.

The Fastnet Lighthouse rises out of the sea, a white spectre, warning all who dare to pass into the vast ocean beyond. I gulp for air, suffocating, an inexplicable fear courses through my veins. I feel the presence of those shadowy people pressing forward for their last glimpse of Irish soil. Overhead the gulls scream like tormented souls. I look down at my hands and realize I am still clutching my ticket. Its edges blacken and the paper crumbles into ash and swirls onto the breeze. Jeremy and Nora are standing beside me. Their tickets also scatter as dust over the foaming Atlantic.

I am brought back to the present by the sound of gulls screeching overhead. An old familiar terror gnaws at the edge of my consciousness. I look around my garden and in the bright sunlight the shadows gradually recede. I am left with a vague sense of apprehension. I must have dozed off. It's been years since I last had that dream. There is no sign of Katie and the boys yet. All this talk of the ship's anniversary is unsettling me. I am swept up in a current of old memories clamouring to surface. I feel powerless to leave the past.

We grew up together a few miles along the coast from Queenstown. Nora and I were inseparable. We both worked at the local fisheries. Making nets was slow, repetitive work and our hands were often raw from the constant rubbing of the rough rope. We often talked of joining the great exodus out of Ireland. Jeremy was Nora's cousin, the youngest of seven children. He worked at the fisheries but lived much closer to Queenstown. He would tell us about the hundreds of people from every part of Ireland who gathered at the port, waiting to set sail to a new life in America. We began to dream of going ourselves. Jeremy urged us to accompany him to New York where his two sisters were already established.

It wasn't hard to convince our families as job opportunities in Ireland were poor. The famine years still cast a long shadow over our lives. With our parents help, we scraped up the money and purchased three third-class tickets. Nora had our futures all mapped out.

"Hannah! You and I will stay with Jeremy's sister until you

get a post and I'll talk to the sisters at the Convent of Mercy," she said.

I hoped to get a housekeeping job or anything to get away from the smell of fish. I could not understand why Nora wanted to travel half-way across the world to closet herself away in a convent.

"Sure nuns out there are different, they teach and work in the community and enjoy life," she laughed.

That girl had an answer for everything. When I told her about my dreams she teased me for being too serious.

"It's only yours nerves. What can happen? Haven't we got a big strapping lad like Jeremy to look after us? We'll have the time of our lives."

Jeremy's house was on the outskirts of Queenstown. We spent our last night there. My parents could not face the quayside, but I knew my mother would be saying the rosary for us most of the day. I'd lost count of how many holy water bottles, spare rosaries and medals she'd packed in my suitcase.

As I lay that last night in Jeremy's house, the dream came to me, stronger and more frightening than before. In the morning, the others seemed to sense my fear and we were a subdued little group as Jeremy's father took us down to the harbour in his pony and trap. He, too, was unusually quiet. This would be his third child to leave these shores.

Approaching the harbour, we stared in wonder at the scene. A couple of miles out to sea, the Titanic lay anchored, aloof and silent, as if too grand to take part in the mayhem at the quayside. As third-class passengers, we would be ferried out on smaller boats together with the mail and luggage. Descending from the trap, we joined this cacophony of joy and sadness as families and friends huddled in last goodbyes. I caught Jeremy's eye and he winked. Lately, I had begun to realize just how much our feelings for each other had deepened. Oh, what was wrong with me? I tried to tell myself it was just the pain of parting from my family, yet at some deeper level I knew it was more, much more. I was terrified. What were these dark shadows threatening everything?

As Jeremy's father turned the pony and trap for home, we joined the surging tide of passengers and market traders, all eager to be first aboard. Pushing our way towards the tender that would ferry us across, I became separated from my companions. Nearing the edge of the quay, I saw Nora and Jeremy were already in the boat. At that moment I became aware I was not moving with the crowd. I could see my friends' faces and hear their voices begging me to climb down. Behind, I could feel the grappling and pushing of the surging throng. I was in danger of being toppled headfirst into the tightly-packed ferry. Suddenly I heard a commanding voice.

"Leave the child alone, she has to go of her own free will."

A slightly-built man in the dark clothes of a priest with a camera strung around his neck was at my side. He shouted to my friends;

"Don't worry; there's plenty of time. She can get one of the smaller boats taking the traders over." He guided me away from the edge. "What is it child, you looked as if you were descending into the fires of hell?"

He introduced himself as Frank Brown, a Jesuit trainee priest. He had just disembarked from the Titanic having travelled from Southampton. He told me he had been invited over to America by a wealthy family he had befriended on board, but his bishop had cabled him, insisting he come home immediately. I told him about the dreams. He looked at me for a while before he said anything. When he spoke, they were not the reassuring words I had expected.

"God works in mysterious ways. Something's not right in your mind, child. Maybe you should wait, there'll be other ships. Your friends will be out there waiting for you."

"But Father! The expense!My parents!I can't not go."

"Let us say a prayer, child. The answer will come to you."

I hear my daughter bringing the boys back from the shore. Their shouts carry on the breeze. I rise to meet them.

"Look what we"ve brought you, Nana," the children shout. Their arms are laden with an assortment of shells and stones. They dump their precious load onto the kitchen step.

"They were trying to outdo each other, looking for the best treasure to bring you back." Katie empties her sagging cardigan pockets to the generous pile covering the step.

Looking at their smiling flushed faces as they examine their loot, I think to myself that maybe it's time I put the past back where it belongs.

"I'm thinking of going back with you to see the new baby."

The boys pay no attention, but Katie looks at me quizzically. "Really?" she says.

"You sound like you mean it this time."

I realise she's right. I do mean it.

I bend down to the boys, flinching at the stiffness in my knee joints. "Shall we pick a really nice shell to take back to your Mammy?" I straighten up again, and listen hard for the sound of the waves, but it's impossible to hear them over the happy babble of the children. Ah well, no matter. The living voices of my great-grandchildren are more precious than those sad whispers from fifty years ago. Yes, it's time to put the past back where it belongs.

MENDING FENCES

BY DONAL A. BUCKLEY,
Silversprings, Cork

Paddy's arrival home for his mother's funeral after an absence of thirty years unlocked many painful memories for family members and for friends and neighbours

MOTHER ALWAYS told us she wanted to go out in style. "Make sure I'm dressed in my blue coat and black shoes. I want my hat on," she would say. "I want to be dressed properly to meet the Lord. He'd expect it of me!"

She looked, as if she was going to Mass, reposing motionless in her coffin with her rosary beads entwined around her fingers.

Friends and neighbours queued in the street, as they slowly entered the Funeral Home to sympathise with the family.

"Sorry for your troubles, Tom!"

"Sorry for your troubles, Mary!"

"Sorry for your troubles, Joan!"

Young and old doing their duty, as boys and girls with scarlet faces shook hands with the family.

Tom called his sisters to the back of the room to meet a man and two young women.

"I want to tell you something," he told them. "Paddy is home!"

"Paddy is home," they cried. "How did he know mother had died," they asked.

"I was always in contact with him," Tom replied. "He flew back from Australia with his two girls. Back to say his mother's Mass. His wife died over three years ago and he went back to a seminary to continue with his studies for the priesthood. He was ordained just a few months ago."

Paddy opened his arms and hugged his two sisters and introduced his daughters to the aunts they had never met. Tom and his sisters returned to the seats reserved for the family as Paddy sprinkled holy water on his mother and made the sign of the cross on her forehead. He joined the local parish priest in the decades of the rosary and prayers for the deceased.

"We're so happy you're back," his sisters told him, as he and Tom prepared to shoulder their mother to the waiting hearse. "She looks so happy," he remarked.

"She's happy now, Paddy," they replied. "Happy you're back to say her funeral Mass."

After her removal to the local church, Paddy and his girls returned to his old home.

"I can remember the morning your mother got the letter from the seminary informing her you were coming out," a neighbour told him. "She arrived at our door with the letter in her hand and a cigarette with a long ash held between her quivering lips. Tears welled in her eyes, as she whispered: "He's coming out! He's coming out!"

"She handed us the letter to read and stared into open space, as if her end was near. If ever I saw despair, I witnessed it that day. A priest in the family, she would say. She looked forward to your first Mass and your first blessing."

"I'll remember that day until I die," Joan told Paddy. "When we got off the bus from work and walked up the narrow lane, we always got the aroma of our dinner, as we neared the house. She had a routine for the dinners: On Monday, she had cold meat and fried potatoes; on Tuesday, we had boiled bacon and cabbage, and Wednesday was her day for roast beef. On Thursdays, the aroma of roast chicken would reach your nostrils half-way up the lane. She always had the salted hake with parsley sauce on a Friday.

"But on that fateful day, there was no aroma coming from her kitchen. When we entered the house, she was slumped on a chair. Her eyes were red from crying and the breakfast dishes were still in the sink. She clasped her blue spotted apron in her hands and all she could say was: "He's coming out, he's coming out!"

"She had you mapped out to be a Parish Priest or maybe a Bishop," Joan said with a smile. "If she could see you now, she'd be so proud of you."

Paddy sensed Joan was trying to break the ice. He hadn't been home in over thirty years. They didn't welcome his wife when he returned home for a visit and they told him she would never be accepted into the family. They didn't approve of the colour of her skin. She cried in the car, as they returned to their hotel. He felt he had let down the two most important women in his life.

But all that changed when his children arrived. When his wife left him and returned to her own people, he had to take on the role of father and mother, as he watched his daughters grow and mature to graduate from Melbourne University with degrees in medicine and law.

Joan was ashen faced, as he recounted his life in Australia.

"What happened to Zeodell," she asked.

"About ten years ago, a truck killed her, as she attempted to cross a highway. The police located the driver, but the courts never convicted him. We attended her funeral service and cremation. Her ashes were scattered in the bush. Since the day she died, I had the urge to return to a seminary and complete my studies for the priesthood. When Rose and Sally graduated from university, I decided to seek their permission to return. I was ordained in Melbourne over three months ago," he told her.

"Your daughters are beautiful," she remarked. "They're a credit to you."

"And what about the colour of their skin," he asked.

Joan blushed and tears flowed from her eyes. "I am so sorry for the way we treated Zeodell and the hurtful remarks we made when you brought her home so many years ago."

Paddy held his sisters hand, as she sobbed and looked at the simple silver cross on the lapel of his jacket. "Are you ever going to forgive us," she asked.

"It's all in the past now. I'll miss sending the Christmas

card to mother," he replied. Paddy walked towards the large bay window. A flock of geese were grazing on the lawn in front of the house. He looked across the valley and pointed to the houses on the hill beyond. "Are these the homes of neighbour's children," he asked.

"I used to live in the white painted house close to the wood," she replied. "John and I went our separate ways about fifteen years ago. I couldn't have children and things didn't work out. He re-married in a registry office and lives with his new wife and family in the house. We're good friends. You'll meet him at mother's funeral Mass to-morrow," she told him with a pallid smile.

Joan reached to the top shelf of a bookcase and produced a photo album. She slipped out a faded wedding photo of their father and mother.

"Where did you get it," he asked.

"We found it after she entered the Care Home when she developed Alzheimer's. We knew there was something wrong, when she started the dinner routine all over again. She seemed to be happy in her own world without a pain or an ache," Joan replied.

"Did she know you before she died," Paddy asked.

"On the day she died, we sat by her bedside until she gasped her last breath. She called your name, as Tom held her hand."

Paddy took a walk down memory lane, as he viewed the photographs in the album. "There she is, seated on a large wooden tub outside the front door in her blue spotted apron and Wellington boots with the collie dog's paws resting on her lap." Paddy studied the photo and smiled. "Isn't she the picture of happiness," he said.

"I have something for you," Joan told him.

He looked across the room, as she opened a small wooden box. He couldn't believe his eyes, when she placed his father's gold pocket watch in his hand. He pressed the gold clasp and the cover sprang open. He wound the spring and to his surprise, the minute hand moved around the dial. He looked at the clock on the mantelpiece and set the pocket watch at the correct time. "I often pressed the gold clasp when I sat on his knee," he recalled.

"He gave it to me to keep for you, until you were ordained a priest. I had to honour his wishes and keep it in a safe place over the years," she told him.

"What am I going to say about her to-morrow," Paddy asked. "There's so much to say."

They sat to the table and discussed old times.

"Do you remember Katie Lyons," Mary asked.

Paddy smiled, as he stirred his tea.

"Your father left a trail of broken hearts when he entered the seminary," Mary told his daughters. "Katie was married when he came out. I think it broke her heart. She died some years later and left a houseful of small children."

"I'm sorry to hear that," Paddy replied. "I'll pray for her to-morrow."

The church was full to capacity long before the appointed hour. The family took up their places in the front seats. Paddy welcomed the congregation and asked them to join the family in the celebration of her life. "She was my mother and I was the son who came out of the seminary, just before I was due to be ordained a priest," he said.

"I know I broke her heart on that terrible day, but time is a great healer and she learned to live with the disappointment, so my sisters tell me. I suppose she's up there now, looking down on us all. She always spoke the best about the departed. I never heard her say a bad word about her neighbours. When I came out, she told me of her disappointment. She resented my decision to leave the seminary."

"What will you do now," she asked.

"Where will you get a job?"

"What will the neighbours say?"

"When I told her I planned to go to Australia and live with my uncle Jack, she seemed to be relieved."

"You'll probably get work there. Your Uncle Jack will look after you, I'll make sure of that," she assured me. "He had to go to Australia, when your father took over the home place from your grandfather. He did well for himself and I'm sure he'll give you every assistance in finding a good job. Your training in the seminary will stand to you," she said.

Paddy told the congregation how his wife had died and spoke of his decision to pursue his studies for the priesthood. "My daughters knew I came out of the seminary many years ago and they had no objection to my going back to pursue my studies for the priesthood," he told them.

"We have on the altar this morning, three of her most treasured possessions: her blue spotted apron, her Wellington boots and her cookbook. She was a loving and caring mother who weathered the storms of life with courage and determination. I know, she'd be so proud of me to-day, to see me back again with my family and neighbours, as I begin to say her funeral Mass. Back again 'mending fences' that will never be broken again."

MEMORIES OF MY TENTH BIRTHDAY

BY MARY GALLAGHER,
Ballisodare, Co. Sligo

*In the frugal fifties, celebrations were rare and a birthday party was
an occasion to be stored in the memory and savoured again and
again*

MANY DAYS of my childhood in the fifties fade into
night's oblivion, but my tenth birthday remains
still etched in my mind and heart. A warm feeling
springs up inside when I recall that day. It was the only
birthday celebrated in my honour. In the hungry forties and the
meagre fifties, struggle and survival left little room for birthday
parties. My birthday celebration was occasioned by a visit of a
favourite aunt for a week-end that happily coincided with the
first Sunday in August, my birthday that year. Fortune looked
kindly on me that day.

On Saturday evening, my mother and aunt collected the
cake in McCann's Bakery in town. After first Mass on Sunday
morning, preparations started. Since the parlour was rarely
used, a spring-cleaning took place that autumn morning.
Cobwebs were removed from nooks and crannies, walls were
brushed down, the floor swept and the dusting done. Windows
wide open, let in fresh air and took out any mustiness that
lingered there.

The furniture consisted of a chaise longue, two fireside chairs
and a table. Two cream and brown china dogs rested on either
end of the mantelpiece. A few chairs were carried upstairs after
dinner. Then the feast was set out. The cake was placed in the
centre of the table; plates of sandwiches stood nearby, Mikado
Biscuits and Cidona completed the variety of food. The china

teapot was taken out as well as some cups, saucers, plates and glasses. Tea was for the adults, Cidona for the children.

The guests were my sister and three girls who lived within walking distance of the house. They arrived at three o'clock in the afternoon bearing gifts of gold, frankincense and myrrh. I received three pairs of white ankle socks with a coloured pattern on the turn-down; a box of white handkerchiefs with flowers embroidered on their corners, and a box of pink perfumed soaps. I felt the richest and most blessed girl in the whole wide world.

As we made our way downstairs to take a tour of the farm, Michael O'Hehir's melodious voice boomed out from the radio in the kitchen where my father and brothers listened to the Sunday match.

The guinea hens were perched high on the roof top. The ducks waddled across the street to quench their thirst at the bar. The collie-dog, Lassie, lay asleep at the entrance to the turf shed, warmed by the autumn sun and filled full with the dinner left-overs. The cattle munched the after-grass in the meadow field. The sheep, newly clipped, dipped and painted, grazed happily on the hillside. The swallows and swifts wheeled in the air and swooped in and out of the hayshed.

We walked down to the stream and sat on moss upholstered rocks, dangling our feet in the water. The clothes flapped on the clothes line. The hens were scratching on the flagstone, picking up and lingering over the last morsel of food. We ran away when we saw the sow rooting outside the pigsty.

We took turns on the seesaw which was a long, thick plank of timber placed over a large even rock by my father. Further down the field a strong rope was suspended between two stout tree branches, a bag of hay lay in the centre as a seat. Here we swung each other on our swing until we grew tired. Ned the donkey leaned his old head over the gate. Knowing he was a quiet animal, we rubbed his nose and let him lick our faces.

As evening approached, we engaged in more feminine pursuits. Sitting under the mountain-ash not far from the house, we picked the red rowan berries that ripened early that year. Using my mothers' sewing basket, we took out number forty thread and darning needles and threaded these beautiful berries into necklaces and bracelets.

It was almost time for the girls to go home. On returning to the house, each got a bag of bull's eyes and marshmallow sweets to take with them. We waved goodbye to Catherine, Mona and Rita. My sister and I went inside to look at my treasures, to smell the scent of pink, perfumed soap and to remember.

No Patriot

By Padraig Foley-O Cleirigh,
Portmarnock, Co. Dublin

*Entrusted with the task of going to town to shop all by himself,
a young boy discovers the excitement and the dangers of his new
world*

BRENDAN'S AUNTS disapproved of father, the patriot historian. Nor were the aunts of great concern to father. "I think those sisters of yours are really Unionists at heart, Kathleen," he once heard father tease mother. "You all had it too soft growing up on that fine farm."

Of course, mother never rose to father's mild raillery. When the patriot died before the twins were nine years old, she was truly heart-broken. Three bullets had never been removed from his left arm and shoulder and he was awarded a military funeral by the authorities. Even this in no way impressed Aunts Margaret and Daisy.

"It's not going to be easy for poor Kathleen now with six young ones to rear," Aunt Margaret sniffed as the cortege moved off.

"At least she has the house and the garden," said Aunt Daisy, who was inclined to be delicate. "Anyway, Kathleen is a strong woman."

Twins Brendan and Elizabeth were the eldest of the family of six and, in the midst of their mourning misery, they found it very odd to hear mother described as being strong because she was of slight build really and not tall at all.

Their house was a two-storey structure that stood at the edge of town. The roof was ornamented with delicate ironwork which ran the length of the building and ended with gold-painted finials. In one of the bedrooms a large map hung incongruously. It showed the thirty –two counties of Ireland in colour. County Tipperary was a golden hue and Co. Waterford was shown in green. Brendan knew that the map had belonged to his father once and wondered how it had been acquired and why it was hanging in the bedroom.Nevertheless, the coloured map was the reason that he and Elizabeth knew the shape of all the counties of Ireland long before they set foot in Kindergarten.

"Goodness me! You're growing like stalks, the two of you. Soon you'll be taller than I am," mother said to them some months after the funeral. She then told them that they were now old enough to be trusted to do downtown chores for her.

"You'll be a great help to me."

Together they visited the baker, the cobbler and the butcher. "Two gigots, a pound of the round, suet and something for the cat," was the regular order for the butcher who used a huge heavy chopper over-enthusiastically to cut through bone and gristle on the massive wooden bench.

"Isn't he scary?" whispered Elizabeth as the ruddy-faced man doubly wrapped their dinner in brown paper just in case its bloody contents oozed some.

"I think he just likes eating his red meat," Brendan said outside the little shop. The two of them giggled all the way home.

Their toughest chore was a trip to the old creamery building which loomed across the river in Co. Waterford. Mother used skimmed milk for baking. Sometimes one of the twins stayed on the County Tipperary side of the river while the other ran across the bridge into Co.Waterford. Then, if no noisy creamery cart arrived, they could talk and laugh and holler at each other across two counties.

"How does the creamery make profit from skimmed milk?" Brendan speculated. For a full can of skimmed milk from the huge vat cost only one ha'penny. Recently his mother had told him all about buying and selling, profit and loss. Businesses that made a profit prospered. At the top of the business world were merchant princes. Some of them might even own cargo ships that exported or imported goods to and from Ireland. Mother said those people were usually rich. That was when he decided that he would become a merchant prince instead of being a patriot like father. He might then marry one of the two beautiful O'Hara girls who wore multi-coloured costumes and won medals for Irish dancing each year at the Feis in Dublin

Not every business in their county town prospered, he was told. If a business made a loss, the owners might be in trouble with the banks. And if they continued to make losses they would have to sell out and the family might go hungry. It was a very tough old world.

But it was also an exciting world as Brendan discovered when the needs of their younger siblings grew so great that Elizabeth had to remain at home to undertake house chores. Now Brendan was entrusted with the task of going to town to shop all by himself. He relished his new status and the freedom to walk through the streets at his own pace and savour all the excitement of business and commerce.

If he left the house early in the morning he could watch strong little donkeys enter the creamery gates, each animal pulling a churn of milk. Their drivers, down from the hills, spoke to one another with loud voices and sat sideways on the carts. When it rained they wrapped jute sacks around their shoulders and puffed Woodbines. Horse-drawn vehicles were able to take four or five churns, and the odd puffing tractor could manage to pull a dozen or so.

Inside the creamery there was banging and clanging. Machine parts were scoured with boiling water until they were immaculately clean. Only then were they re-assembled and the machinery moved slowly through the processes of making butter.

Sometimes, while he waited for the creamery office to open, Brendan watched the butter-maker operate a machine that cut and wrapped the great sheets of gold automatically.

"You can stand there next the door and watch all you want. But don't you be getting in my way, Sonny," the man warned.

The creamery manager's middle–aged and unmarried

daughter was in charge of the office and, although she often looked sad and fatigued, she always stamped his coupon with a smile and told him that she had known his patriot father well - a long time ago.

Carrying a full can of skimmed milk was no easy task. His can had only a wire handle.He used a clean handkerchief to prevent red weals rising on the palms of his hand. But as he trudged homewards he had to change the hand carrying the heavy skimmed milk every two hundred yards or so. Sometimes he forgot the protective handkerchief. Then the wire bit into his fingers until both hands became red, raw and wrinkled.

There was a choice of three routes to take him back to the house. The first route took him through the main street of the town which was named after O'Connell, the Liberator. The street was like a long tie-box, closed at each end and sheltered by tall shops on either side. At one end of the busy street was the famous West Gate and at the other end the equally famous Main Guard.

Three shops in O'Connell Street held his attention.The first was a fishing-rod and gun store. It had a distinctive odour of gun-metal and fishing tackle and a wondrous display of colourful flies. There he lingered a long minute before moving in front of the gleaming cycles in Brady's Shop. When the good times came again he knew exactly which sleek, black Raleigh he would buy. The next stop was Woolworths:paradise itself. Though sorely tempted, he was ashamed to slip into the store for a minute and possibly be seen carrying a can of skimmed milk by the beautifully groomed O'Hara girls. He knew they also loved to wander around the store.

The second route brought him to Mary Street and by a house where the writer, Anthony Trollope, once lived. Across the street were strong railings guarding Old St. Mary's where in 1539 eleven bishops took an oath of loyalty to Henry V111 of the many wives. At Henry's Court a local song, Cailín Óg cois tSiúire mé was popular.

Morton Street was the most interesting place along this second route. It was here during the great siege that the flower of Cromwell's invincible army endured terrible chain shot from two artillery pieces.

Further along the road, past crowded flats, were more immediate dangers. Dermot Finley's gang frequently lurked behind the hedges ready to harass and bully him. However, if they saw his impedimentum – the heavy can of skimmed milk – the attack was called off. Dermot, son of a garda siochána, knew there would be repercussions for himself if his war-game interfered with any boy or girl carrying out domestic chores.

The third route went along the quays and the bacon-curing factory. Here the screaming of swine being slaughtered reached his ears and sometimes the stench of offal assaulted his nose. In order to avoid the unwelcome sounds and smells, he walked along the other side of the road by the river and the sets of steps that led down to the water where barges once moored.

One sunny morning he dawdled at the bottom of the first set of white steps and watched the dark green water grass wriggle and trail downstream. It was not long before he dipped his hand into the current to feel the surging water flow through his fingers. That was when the new thought exploded in his head.

He put the empty can floating on the water before snatching it back to safety. From that day forward every time he took the river route to the creamery he played his new game.In a short time he became an expert at letting the can float the whole length of the steps and then grabbing it from the current at the last moment.

One day the river was in flood. The can floated across the steps at surprising speed. Twice he grabbed it out of the water in the nick of time, but at the third attempt his fingers slipped off the rim and the vessel inexorably floated away. He ran down to the next set of steps and waited for the can to come by.When he stretched out his body over the water his fingers touched the metal side but the can slipped out of his grasp and slowly sailed down river towards the third and last set of steps.

There was just one more chance left to grab the vessel out of swirling water. Then, when the can floated by, he eased a stick over the side of the rim and slowly drew it towards the bottom step. As he gentled it ashore his hand, arm and shoulder ached terribly and he could feel the thin stick bend under the force of the current. Another inch or two ... Suddenly the stick buckled and the can was forever lost. For one wild moment he thought he might jump into the rushing water to retrieve it. But he could not swim and here at the Gashouse Bridge the river seemed to be bottomless.

He sat dejectedly on the steps. There was nothing for it but to go back home without can or skimmed milk and face the wrath of his mother, an encounter he dreaded even more than Dermot Finley and his gang.

He found his younger sister, Kate, swinging on the gate
"You're in for it," she hissed delightedly.

The news had already travelled.

Mother moved towards him, her face stony white.

Then, to his utter astonishment, she folded him tightly in her arms.

"That old can wasn't worth losing you, Brendan."

LOOSE LEAVES

By LINDA GUERIN,
St. Patrick's Road, Limerick

With the attitude of a person selecting a Sunday newspaper, the elderly gentleman picked up cabbage leaf after cabbage leaf, studying each one with great care

IN 1960S LIMERICK many people lived on tight budgets. Money was scarce and every item purchased had to be essential for the household. Sometimes penny-pinching led to limited choices.

One day in a grocer's shop when I was around six or seven, I made a discovery. A wicker-basket sat on the floor in front of the counter. It was filled to the point of bursting with a consignment of diminutive, emerald-green vegetables. They looked like miniature cabbages.

Other customers in the shop were buying them. I decided to pick one up and study it. I wondered what it tasted like. Then I turned and showed the dainty vegetable to my mother.

"Why don't we buy some of these tiny cabbages," I asked.

"No," she said, holding a large, dark-green cabbage in her hands, "you wouldn't like them."

Years later I bought some of the miniature cabbages, otherwise known as Brussels sprouts and tasted them for myself. My mother was wrong. I loved them. They were delicious.

Nowadays, many cabbages purchased in supermarkets have been hermetically sealed in clear, plastic wrap.

When I was a child, supermarkets were modest in size and few in number. More often than not, people bought their vegetables from grocers with local suppliers. As a result, the fresh-from-the-fields cabbages sometimes harboured unwanted wildlife.

The first signs of their presence were the perfectly round holes on the outer, dark-green leaves. On closer inspection, slugs were usually found dozing amongst the folds of the cabbage.

Country spiders turned up as well, having been unwittingly transported into town with the vegetables. They were usually released into the wild, in other words our back-yard, by one of my parents.

I remember one wet, Saturday morning my mother and I set off for the grocer. Dressed in our winter coats and armed with an umbrella and shopping bags, we made our way through the rain.

The sky was hidden behind a blanket of grey, storm-clouds. Gusts of wind made it difficult to hold onto the umbrella. At the traffic-lights, the windscreen wipers of the cars and vans were swishing back and forth and pedestrians hurried across the road to avoid the downpours.

The shop was empty when we arrived. My mother immediately fell into conversation with the grocer about the bad weather while I wandered around the shop with my dripping-wet umbrella.

Large heads of cabbages, bunches of bright orange carrots, strings of golden onions and cardboard boxes of lettuces caught my eye as I inspected the shelves and sacks that lined the walls.

I stopped at an old, timber chest which was resting on the floor at the entrance to the shop. Curiosity got the better of me. I stood on tip-toes and peeked inside the chest to see what vegetables it might contain. To my surprise, I found that the chest was filled to the brim with the dark-green, outer leaves of cabbages.

Some of the loose leaves were in tatters. Others were dotted with holes. I picked one up and ran my fingers over its deep veins. Then I heard my name being called.

I turned my head and saw my mother beckoning to me. She wanted me to help her with the vegetables. She packed potatoes into her bag and gave me a fine specimen of a cabbage to carry home.

At that moment an elderly gentleman entered the grocer's shop. He stopped at the timber chest and began to examine its contents. He was grey-haired and slightly stooped. The shoulders of his baggy overcoat were wet from the recent shower and raindrops stood on the edge of his turned-up collar like little glass beads.

With the attitude of a man selecting a Sunday newspaper, he picked up cabbage leaf after cabbage leaf, studying each one with great care.

My mother said "goodbye" to the grocer and saluted the man on the way out of the shop. He nodded his head.

THE BLACK SACK

By RICHARD S. CAHILL,
Cahir, Co. Tipperary

Perhaps it was his father's tendency to disorder that triggered in Casey the need for symmetry and neatness of numbers, a need he felt himself more in the grip of as the years went by

PUTTING THE dog to sleep was one of the hardest things he'd ever had to do, but at nineteen years of age, deaf, blind and towards the end, incontinent, the vet's wisdom was that it would be a kindness to send him gently off.

Waiting all day for five o'clock to come - the time arranged on the phone - had been worse than anything that followed. In and out to the little tin-roofed shed at the back of the dairy, where Sam lay cold-nosed and shivering in spite of the old anorak Casey had drawn snugly around him. In and out, in and out he went, every minute an hour, stroking the icy, doomed muzzle, saying his goodbyes.

At least, when the vet arrived, exactly on time, it had been quick. Barely a third of the yellow liquid had been squeezed into a vein in the old dog's leg when, without so much as a whimper, he had taken his leave.

Despite being well bred, from a mother who excelled at moving cattle around the farm and a father who had won prizes at sheepdog trials, Sam proved useless as a working dog. He fooled around the yards, chased the hens and padded to the back door for his food while over the years a succession of willing peers did the hard graft and paid for their keep. In the long run, he would out-live all of them. Casey was forty-seven when Sam arrived as a pup, and together the two of them would grow old.

It was because Sam hated going out into the fields so much that he eventually took to bringing him for walks along the narrow, winding lane that tortuously led to the main road. It came as a surprise to Casey that he began to enjoy these walks, as if he hadn't trudged enough around his fields all day. But living on his own since his mother died, often without another human to talk to for days on end, the lane became a lifeline to the world outside.

He'd found it strange at first. "Isn't it grand for you, with your dog and lead, taking your constitutional like a bank manager," Williams at the crossroads remarked. The crossroads marked the furthest point of their evening stroll. Williams's comments irked him, and the temptation was there to turn back before reaching his neighbour's house, but he persisted and found he could give as good as he got.

"You're not too busy yourself, by the looks of it," he'd smile. "Sure we're both gentlemen of leisure now and don't we deserve to be at our age?" The first time he said this, Williams coloured and Casey felt he'd won a small victory. A draw was eventually conceded and he was surprised to find that the odd evening Williams didn't appear at his gate as he approached, he'd feel a tinge of disappointment.

On a whim one day, he had counted the number of paces to the crossroads. Williams, hands stuffed into his trouser-pockets and a heavy woollen scarf around his neck in spite of the warmth of the evening, was waiting for him. From twenty paces, he greeted Casey: "A warm one, Charlie. We'll never stick this heat, sure the country is parched."

Casey was still counting. "One thousand, six hundred and ninety-three, ninety-four, ninety-five, " he said, kicking lightly the bottom rail of Williams's gate on ninety-five.

"Is it your money you're counting, Charlie? Or is the heat after getting to you?"

"Near enough a mile from my place to yours," Casey answered. "It's a two-mile round-trip every evening for myself and the dog. I didn't think it was as far as that."

"There you are now," Williams said, "It's important to know things like that."

Casey shrugged off the sarcasm, but kept from Williams another oddity his counting had uncovered. At five hundred and thirty-three paces from his own front gate, he had passed, on his left, Sheehan's Nissan car, parked tail-to-road, facing the door of the ramshackle cottage. And five, three, three, were the digits on the Nissan's number-plate, which struck him as one of life's inexplicable coincidences. Casey had always been like that, noticing little things others would pass without the slightest thought. It had been on the tip of his tongue to tell Williams, but now he was glad he didn't. Williams, sometimes, was too smart for his own good.

Perhaps it was his father's tendency to disorder, indeed chaos, around the yards and fields of his upbringing, which triggered in Casey the need for the symmetry and neatness of numbers, a need he felt himself more and more in the grip of as the years went by. As a young lad, he found himself constantly picking up what his father had so casually dropped, tidying buckets or implements or empty feedstuff bags scattered here and there, and later, in silent, growing resentment, fixing sagging gates, hammering nails into galvanised sheets to stop them rattling in the wind and keeping him awake at night.

"Is the dog sick or what?" Williams asked one evening after Casey had borne Sam, still wrapped in the old anorak, to the grave he had dug for him in the orchard.

"He's gone off for himself. The vet said it'd be a kindness. I miss him like hell, though."

"You would. You'd be fierce attached to an old dog. The Missus here wouldn't let one near the place, afraid of her life of a dog."

He'd settled him nicely into the hole under one of the apple trees. The tree was older than Sam but would be there to give him shade long after Casey himself was gone. He touched the cold muzzle a last time, drew the anorak down and began to shovel back the earth. Patting the sods neatly into place on top, he knew he would never again keep a dog.

Venturing onto the road without Sam felt as strange in the beginning as the first evening he'd walked out with him. The absence of the well-worn lead running through his fingers was hard to get used to. Sam's shambling, meandering gait at his side, the sudden ditch-bound lunge when he smelled a rabbit, his own small urgings or reprimands as they moved in the quiet of the lane, were absences keenly felt.

Nevertheless, Casey soon enough settled into taking his evening stroll alone. The habit had become so embedded while the dog was alive, that it seemed natural for him to continue doing so now that Sam was gone.

Still, the dog's passing changed something in Casey. There was a sense of control being lost. A hole had been punched through the grinding, yet accepted routine of his life around sheds and fields. For years, the old dog and he had lived side by side - chunks of their days marked off by his duties of care to the animal, the obligation to let him out first thing in the morning, to feed and walk him, to comb the tangles from his thick, unruly coat and, last thing at night, to lock him safely in the barn. What had seemed unchanging and constant for so long was shown to be all too easily turned to dust.

It may have been this sense of control slipping from him, or no more, perhaps, than a way to avoid thinking too much about the uncertainties which lay ahead, that caused him to apply himself more rigorously than ever to the orderliness of his house and farm. Everything in its place and a place for everything was the quiet, insistent mantra he worked to. If he could keep order in the familiar, everyday bits of his life, the disorder and uncertainty of the future might somehow be held at bay.

He set about hiring a man to spray-paint the farm buildings, which seemed suddenly shabby and neglected. Moss had taken hold in the front yard where years ago tarmac had been laid. Sulphate of iron was mixed with sand and evenly spread, dead moss swept up and taken away in the wheelbarrow. All day, every day, until it was time to go for his walk along the road in the evening, Casey worked on keeping things in order.

The lane became an extension of his neatly ordered world. He found it upsetting, on leaving the comforting exactitude inside his gate, to be confronted with the litter he sometimes came upon among the hedgerows. It was an affront to the sense of order and control he so desperately sought. To ignore a sweet-wrapper caught in briars, a crisp bag scudding ahead of him on the road was to ignore the disorder and chaos he hated.

"People have no respect anymore," he said when he came to the crossroads one evening. "No respect for anyone or anything."

"What makes you say that," Williams asked.

Casey didn't answer. He'd been looking forward to his walk, to having a chat with Williams, but now, instead, he felt cheated and angry. Coming along the road it had been a beautiful, crisp evening, frost already glinting on the small stones under his feet, the sky in the west ablaze with tomorrow's promise. For a few hundred yards he'd walked briskly, getting the blood going, breathing in air that was pure and clean.

He'd passed Sheehans, the car exactly where it always was; the bend where a lone birch drooped so low that he touched its bare, silver branches and felt the bite of frost on his fingers. Up the little hill, past the entrance to the wood on the left, the stream chuckling through it unseen, its murmur part of the music of this lovely place, he'd felt quietness seep into him.

And then, abruptly, the spell was broken. In the centre of the road, on its grassy spine, lay a bulging, overflowing, black plastic sack, its ugliness so incongruous, so jarringly out of place in the symmetry of Casey's world that its presence made him gasp aloud.

He would have liked to feel close enough to Williams to be able to explain why he said people have no respect. But what he wanted to say was stuck somewhere too deep down for him to be able to draw it to the surface.

"What makes you say that," Williams persisted. "That people have no respect? "

"Ah, nothing, nothing. Forget it."

Williams didn't pursue it any further. "You'll come in for the cup of tea anyway. Herself has it made inside."

"I'm only after it. Some other time." He was too upset now to face into Williams's house, to try to engage in polite conversation.

On his way home, he came upon the sack again. It was too

heavy to carry. He twisted its black neck into a knot, pushed it into the ditch where frost had already stiffened the grass. Tomorrow he'd bring some smaller bags and fill them with the vileness he knew was there. Little by little, over the coming days, he would get rid of everything. Order would be restored.

It was a losing battle, of course. The black sack and its contents could be disposed of, rubbish thrown from passing cars gathered up, the lane kept clean for as long as he'd be able to do so, but disarray and chaos would win out in the end. Nothing he did would change that. The futility of even trying filled him now with an immense weariness. The night closed in around him. Sam was under the big apple tree in the orchard and there he would sleep all the long, silent hours that stretched out ahead.

Casey trudged homewards, thinking what it must be like to sleep as Sam now slept, beyond the reach of all that troubled him this night.

THE BRIGHT BERRIES OF CHRISTMAS

BY ROY GAMBLE,
Hillsborough, Co. Down

A week before Christmas – for Christmas came in its proper season then – I would collect my father's billhook and set out to cut the holly

W HEN I WAS twelve, we lived on the top of a hill about a mile from the town and rejoiced in the quaint address: Cock Crow Knowe, Drumbroneth, Dromore, County Down. My parents were hale and hearty and I still had four brothers.

That year I inherited the job of bringing home the Christmas holly. There were two sites. The best one was the farthest away where the female of a pair of trees produced beautiful berries in a hedge on a sloping field that ran down to Ballaney bog on Jinny Jamison's farm.

Baxter's Forth – really a ring-fort or iron-age rath – was the other site, but the holly here was more bush than tree and the berries were never as big or as shiny or as plentiful. There was also a lone tree, with pale, variegated leaves growing among the hazel and the birch and the ivy-covered oaks. It never produced berries, but it was still highly-prized for the variety it added to the wreath my mother made to hang on the front door.

She was unique in this, for no-one else in the neighbourhood hung Christmas wreaths on their doors. I think it was an American custom she got from her cousin, Emma, who lived in Philadelphia.

On a day in late November – it always seemed to be when

the trees and hedgerows were shrouded and elongated with columns of mist – I would call-up our old border collie and we'd cross the fields to check out the sites. I was always fearful that the weather would change and there would be hard frosts, for then the blackbirds and the thrushes and the Scandinavian redwings and fieldfare would flock on the holly trees and strip the berries in a single day.

A week before Christmas – for Christmas came in its proper season then – I would go out to the shed and cut lengths of twine and collect my father's billhook and go and cut the holly. Coming home, I kept to the fields to avoid neighbours begging sprigs of holly to stick behind pictures or display in vases, for there was little money at that time to fritter away on Christmas decorations.

I had a paper round then out of Reid's Newsagents in Dromore and I swelled my Christmas tips selling to several old ladies on my route holly at half-a-crown a bunch. I bought a Timex wristwatch for three pounds two and sixpence. It had a black face and numerals that glowed in the dark. It was only worn on Sundays and special occasions, but I would take it out each day to admire it and polish the face and to make sure it was properly wound.

On Christmas morning we five brothers would walk, line abreast, up the Drumbroneth road as far as the little stream that marked the dividing line between the townlands of Drumbroneth and Ballaney.We always timed our arrival back home to see a flush-faced mother bending to take the roasting pan from the oven of the coal-fired Modern Mistress range, and father mashing potatoes with the big wooden beetler that was worn smooth with years of potato pounding.

In the afternoon, the wind-up gramophone with the wooden casing that smelt of varnish when it heated up, was brought out and we'd listen to Paul Robeson's "October winds lament around the Castle of Dromore", foolishly imagining that he was singing about our own home town, and the wheedling, nasal voice of Delia Murphy: "If I were a blackbird I'd whistle and sing" and "The Old Groaner" himself: "I'm dreaming of a white Christmas" and we'd sing along to the Glasgow Orpheus choir and all the lovely, old, familiar carols.

As the afternoon fell away and the evening drew on and it began to grow dark, the two oldest brothers, Jack and Bob, got ready to walk to Dromore for the first house of the pictures.

When they went out, you could feel the cold come in through the open door and you shivered a little and felt a fleeting feeling of sadness because the warmth and completeness that had wrapped itself round our family circle that day was suddenly broken, and you knew, no matter how much you longed for it not to change, that all things must pass and nothing stays the same.

But, like the bright, red berries of the holly hanging on the front door and shining up there on the picture frames in that cottage kitchen, the light of those childhood Christmases will burn in my memory forever.

The Contrary Woman

By Sheila Doris,
Bedford, England

Ailish succeeded in engaging the late straggler on the bus in conversation, only to be told: 'You're the most aggravating woman I have ever laid eyes on.'

THE BUS was ready to leave. Ailish could see the back indicator lights flashing. She was a good runner but the weight of two laden shopping bags slowed her down. She shouted in desperation: "Wait for me, wait!" Luckily, the driver spotted her in the side mirror and did wait.

"Thanks," she gasped as the door opened.

"It's yerself is it?" the driver remarked out of an impassive face, his solid bulk comfortably spread behind the wheel.

Ailish searched for her purse. She felt like saying "If it's not meself who do you think it is?" but she held her tongue and paid for her ticket.

"A few more years and you'll be havin' your bus pass," the driver said in a conciliatory fashion as he handed her some change.

Ailish went red. She was ten years off having her bus pass.

"I suppose you will as well," she returned.

"Aye, then we can go on a trip somewhere, anywhere. Wouldn't that be grand?"

Ailish stuffed her purse into a pocket saying: "And what would your wife say to that, I wonder." "Oh, she'd pull me hair out – that's for sure."

Ailish looked at his shiny bald head and laughed. People smiled at her as she side-stepped half-way down the bus to get a seat.

With a sigh of relief, she sat down and put her shopping on the seat next to her. She was feeling tired and hot and not in the best of form. She wondered vaguely if it was the menopause and how long it went on for. Some said it went on for years.

Just as the bus was about to leave, a late straggler rapped on the closed door and was allowed in. As he stood looking to see if there was an empty seat, some people regarded him curiously. The face wasn't familiar.

The only seat available had Ailish's bags on it. Hurriedly, Ailish grabbed her bags, put one on her lap and the other on the floor between her legs.

The man settled himself beside her. She eyed his large carrier bag. It was from a shop that sold men's clothes and nothing else. The clothes in the window of that shop didn't have price tags. People had to go in if they were looking for something in particular and they seldom came out with one arm as long as the other.

She glanced sideways at him. He was all in black He must be a priest, she thought, either that or he liked to be very dreary – not a speck of colour on him. She took a closer look. His eyes were green and there were specks of grey in his dark hair. At least that's something, she thought.

He said nothing to her so she felt she had to say something. It was a compulsion of hers. Silence worried her.

"Sorry about the bags, Father."

He turned and looked at her. "I'm not a 'father'".

"Oh, sorry! I thought you were a priest. Are you not? Was it a funeral you were at? Sometimes you only see relatives at funerals, or weddings. I saw a lovely wedding dress in a window today. It had long lace sleeves, but I suppose you wouldn't be interested in that. Were you on holiday? You look very brown."

A dark flush crept up from his neck on to his face. He did not reply. She had noted that his trousers were too long and that his jacket was not a good fit. The neck of his black shirt was open. Perhaps that didn't fit either. Perhaps he had murdered a priest and taken his clothes.

It seemed like everyone on the bus was waiting for his reply.

He took a pipe out of his pocket and stuck it in his mouth.

Ailish was on the point of saying: "You're not allowed to smoke," but something about the set of his face stopped her.

"You are the most aggravatin' woman I have ever laid eyes on," he said between his teeth.

"Am I? Well, you can't have met many women if you think I'm aggravatin!"

They exchanged a hostile look. Ailish went red. She loved his voice, so deep and yet soft as well.

After a few minutes of quiet, Ailish introduced herself. The suspicion of a smile lifted the corner of his mouth and he nodded, the pipe still held firmly between his teeth.

It looked like he wasn't going to be talkative so she asked him his name.

"Daniel – Daniel Clabby."

This was what people wanted to know and they settled back in their seats and wondered which Clabby family he belonged to.

"Oh no," Ailish muttered.

Daniel looked at her.

"I forgot to get a barm-brack," she explained.

He took the pipe out of his mouth. "Can't you do without it?"

"I suppose I could, but it's Hallowe'en and I wanted to get the ring."

"What childish nonsense," he said. She looked at the hands nursing the bowl of the pipe. They were large and weather-beaten.

"I know, but my mother gets the ring every year and I was hoping I would get it this year."

He put the pipe back between his teeth and bit on the stem, seemingly deep in thought.

"Where do you live?"

"Near the Cross Keys," she told him.

"Then come to tea. Bring your mother. My brother always has a brack on Hallowe'en."

"And does he ever get the ring?"

"Every year – there's no one but himself, but I'll be there this time."

"So he has a barm-brack all to himself?"

"As far as I know, unless a parishioner calls when he's having his tea."

"A parishioner?"

"He's the parish priest," Daniel explained.

"Oh!"

"Mm." And the pipe went back into his mouth.

On Sunday afternoon, Ailish and her mother called at the presbytery.

Ellie Malloy, the housekeeper, opened the door. "Hello Rose-Ann and Ailish. Come on in. I'll be off meself shortly so don't be offended when I disappear," she said pushing back a stray grey hair and pulling up her trousers.

They all sat in the living room.

Daniel looked like a different person. She was lost for words as she looked at him, but Rose-Ann knew Father Peter well and they talked about coffins and wills and land and all the diseases that beset people.Ailish was glad when Ellie Malloy came in saying the tea was ready and that she was off.

"Thanks, Ellie. We'll see you tomorrow, please God," Father Peter said as he stood up and straightened his long back.

"Oh, you will, Father. You will unless I fall into a coma and drown meself in dreams," Ellie said with a laugh and a wink at Ailish as she took her leave.

Ailish blinked. What was the woman winking at her for? Maybe she hadn't been winking. Maybe she had a hair in her eye.

She looked at Daniel as she stood up and decided to be sensible. "I'll do the washing up," she said.

Daniel looked down on her. "Indeed, you will not. I'm well able to wash up a few cups."

They went into the big kitchen which was lovely and cosy with a black range and a dresser filled with colourful crockery. The table was set and the teapot kept warm with a knitted cosy.

Ailish saw that the barm-rack was already sliced. No chance

of cheating there. She took it upon herself to pour the tea, and Rose-Ann took the first slice of barm-brack.

"Childish nonsense," Daniel Clabby called it as he felt his slice for the ring.

Ailish could hardly believe it when she found the ring in her slice of barm-brack. She removed the greaseproof paper from around it and pushed it on to her finger. And then she smiled at everyone in triumph.

Rose-Ann let her away with it. After all, there was still one in their kitchen. She'd bought it from the shop at the petrol station days ago and had hidden it as she was prone to terrible temptation and would have wolfed down the whole brack if it was anywhere in sight. Oh yes, there were times when she'd hidden sweets from herself only to go mad searching for them when she'd forgotten where she'd hidden them.

The barm-brack was on her mind as they went home. It was still safe. She had not forgotten where it was. No, she had not forgotten and she fully intended to have the ring on her finger before the day was out.

There was a lot of speculation about why Daniel Clabby had been wearing his brother's old clothes. The pubs were rife with talk of all the possibilities. The women whispered together.

All this must have got back to Father Peter Clabby because on the Sunday, after he'd said Mass, he had something to say. He was a serious sort of a person and the people drew their breath in when he mentioned his brother. Then he explained that Daniel had spent his life as a fisherman and that the clothes he had arrived in had been eaten by cows when he'd gone for a swim in the river.

Someone tittered. Father Peter smiled and the whole congregation exploded in gales of laughter.

This story was told and retold and elaborated on so it was some time before Daniel had the courage to call on Ailish.

It was Christmas time and the decorations were up and the crib was in the corner of the room on a small table.

From the moment she opened the door to Daniel, Ailish could

not stop talking. Her mother had to take over and make the tea

At last Daniel got a word in. "I see you're still wearing that ring."

Just then the mother called: "Come in, it's ready!"

Ailish hid her blushes as they went into the kitchen and pulled out the chairs.

Her mother held up her hand. "Look, I got a ring too."

"Indeed! Some people have all the luck," he said sadly, They didn't know whether he was serious or not.

"Ah sure, drink yer tae. Things could be worse," the mother ordered.

"I miss the smell of the sea," Daniel confided.

Ailish's mother threw a bit of ham on the floor for the cat. "Sure you can smell the cows and the grass and the rain in the wind."

A little while later Ailish and Daniel walked up the lane together.

"I think about you sometimes," Ailish said. She was not going to tell him that she thought about him every night.

"Do you?"

"Yes. Your trousers are too long and you should stop smoking."

"I have given up the sea, but I am not giving up me pipe," he retorted and then in a gentler voice he added, "I can't stop thinking about you."

It was the nicest thing that had ever been said to her. For once, she was lost for words.

"Well, I'm sure you think about other people too," she replied, and she was thinking of Mrs Quinn's very good-looking daughter. She'd noticed Daniel talking to her on the main street.

Daniel was mystified. "I suppose I do think about others, doesn't everybody?"

"What about Bridget Quinn's daughter?"

Daniel was surprised. "I never saw her before I saw her last week."

They stood looking at each other. Daniel was not sure whether he should kiss her or not and Ailish was thinking that she'd gone too far.

"Good night, then," Daniel said.

Ailish watched him go. "That's it then. I'm never goin' to see him again," she thought.

Later, in his brother's house, Daniel sat by the fire smoking his pipe and looking thoughtful.

His brother prodded the coals into life and put another few sods of turf around the fire.

"You're a quiet one. When did you start seein' Ailish Hannify?"

Daniel smiled ruefully.

"Well, when did you," his brother Peter insisted.

Daniel was quiet for a minute and then he said: "She said that she thinks of me sometimes."

His brother laughed. "That should be enough for you."

This eased Daniel's mind.

They sat in comfortable silence for a while. Then Daniel asked: "What about Patsy Quinn? Has she agreed to sing at Midnight Mass?"

"Father Peter smiled in reply. "Yes, we are honoured. She has the voice of an angel."

Ailish's mother cross-questioned her daughter. "Are you going out with him?"

"I said some stupid things. I probably won't see him again," Ailish said as she settled her mother for the night.

"What did he say to you," her mother wanted to know.

What Daniel had said to her was something that she wanted to store in her heart for ever. It was between themselves.

"He said 'goodnight then'."

"There's something you're not telling me," her mother complained.

"It never started, so it never ended," Ailish said calmly though her heart was sore.

But Ailish was wrong. Daniel became a regular visitor to the house.

Spring came. The trees enveloped themselves in shades of

green. The warmth of the summer came and, with it, the smells of wild flowers beneath blue skies.

Ailish and Daniel sometimes met in the town and they were seen down Lovers' Lane - a shady boreen that led to a small wood where a stream gushed over rocks and stones.

And then autumn came with her shades of copper and gold. Soft mists kissed the hedges in the first hours of the day. Gossamer webs hung between leaves where shining droplets like jewels caught the light. And birds flitted, too quick for the eye.

The days were mild as the first leaves started to fall. Wild roses blossomed in the hedges, blackberries hung on to the bushes. It was on such a mild day as they walked in the dappled shade of the trees that Daniel asked Ailish to be his wife.

And so before another Oiche Shamhna had passed there was a real gold ring on her finger, and Daniel married the most aggravatin' woman he had ever laid eyes on.

TIM THE SOLDIER

BY CHRISTY WADE,
Ballycahill, Co. Tipperary

The night a ten-year-old was recruited for an important mission by a veteran of the First World War

VETERANS OF the First World War have by now, in this year of two thousand and twelve, gone the way of the horse-drawn cart, the corncrake and the fireside cricket. They have vanished from the scene.

Fifty years ago almost every parish in Ireland had one or maybe two such men, who had fought and luckily survived the horror that was trench warfare and returned home to pick up the thread of life in their native place as best they could.

A certain aura of mystery often surrounded these men, especially for young boys who would hear their elders say: "That fellow was in Flanders or at the Somme in the great war," and stories would be told, in hushed tones, of bayonet charges and rifle fire and bombs and hand grenades and poison gas, all of which would highly charge the imaginations of us ten and twelve-year-olds.

These veterans were, in general, men who largely kept to themselves, and were regarded by us boys at the time with a certain amount of awe.

Such a man lived in our village - a man who was known as Tim the Soldier. He was a tall, upright, straight-standing man with a fierce mustache, and he wore a peaked cap under which beamed bright eyes from which nothing could hide.

He lived at the edge of the village across from, and a little down from, the church, and beside the school. At the other end of the village was the shop which stocked all the local necessities and also had a lone Shell petrol pump to serve the half-dozen or so cars which were in the parish at the time. This pump stood at the point of the turn on the road, an ideal location from which the whole village could be observed. So, between the Shell petrol pump, with its bright yellow head, and Tim the Soldier's gate, no move could be made unobserved within the confines of the village.

Like most men of his age and time he smoked a pipe. For the primary purpose of keeping the pipe fueled, he carried at all times a razor-sharp pen-knife with two blades, of which the smaller was the sharpest and used for cutting little flakes off the jot of tobacco. The bigger blade was used for other jobs like peeling apples or cutting potatoes in half to increase the quantity of seed at planting time in the little garden he maintained with fork and shovel at the side of his house.

Another piece of equipment he was never without was an early version of a cigarette lighter, which was fueled by petrol and ignited by twirling a notched steel wheel with the thumb. This wheel ground on a piece of flint which created sparks near the wick and after several tries lit-up the lighter, often with a burst of angry flame and a plume of black smoke.

At that time, we had at the head of our parish, a priest with a great devotion to Our Blessed Lady and, in her honour, on a particular night each week a novena was held. Everybody, without exception, was expected, and indeed did turn up for prayers, as they were known.

One night when I was about ten years old, I arrived at great speed on my mother's bike a little behind time, and, as I parked the bike outside Tim's house, he startled me by appearing suddenly at the other side of the wall and he said gruffly: "Where are you going?" to which I replied I was going to prayers.

Tim said: "You can forget about that, they are all gone in and you are late. Besides, I want your help in an important mission. I want you to look out for the enemy while a very important manoeuvre is carried out."

This conjured up, in my young mind, all kinds of exciting

military-type possibilities and I immediately asked what I was to do. I was then told to cycle my bike up near the petrol pump and stay there and, if I saw anyone coming, I was to whistle as loudly as I could. I faithfully moved into position as instructed, but I was more interested in what Tim was doing than in keeping a lookout.

Tim made his way to the school gate where was parked one of the few cars around at the time, a Ford Prefect. Tim took from his pocket a Baby Power whiskey bottle from which he removed the screw cap. He next produced a length of string on which he had formed a loop at one end. He secured the loop around the neck of the little bottle and he unscrewed the petrol cap from the Ford Prefect. He gently lowered the bottle into the petrol tank and let it fill and then he slowly withdrew the full bottle from the tank and replaced the petrol cap on the car, screwed the cork securely on the bottle and gave me the all-clear sign and moved back down towards home.

I quickly followed on the bike to see what great things he would do with the bottle of petrol. I caught up with Tim just as he was going in his gate, and asked what he intended to do with the petrol. "Do you want it to make a bomb?" To which Tim replied: "I do not. I want it for my lighter."

First And Last Love

By Mary Dwyer,
Glasnevin North, Dublin

Tom Kelly was a mysterious presence in our house, though the only evidence of him was his name in a lovely book. Eventually, all was revealed

" MAMMY, WHO IS TOM KELLY?" was a question I frequently asked as a child. Invariably, the answers ranged from: "Put that book back and go out to play" or "Lay the table quickly, the tea is nearly ready" or "Be careful with that book."

The book in question was "Works of William Shakespeare." It was exquisitely bound with soft, maroon Moroccan leather. The pages were edged with gold and the print was small but very clear.

It was the most beautiful book in our home. My mother told us that she had sent away to London for it when she was single. But on the fly-leaf was the name "Tom Kelly." This always intrigued me. Who was this Tom Kelly whose name was written on my mother's book? Hence the question that remained unanswered for years.

When I was eleven, I was on holiday in Kerry with my grandparents. One day while walking with my aunt, I heard her call out to a man across the narrow street: "Hello Tom, this is Peg's daughter."

He shouted back: "My, she's good-looking, just like her Mom."

I preened a bit, but thought no more of it until we got back to the house.

"We met Tom Kelly on the street", my aunt told my grandmother. "He's home from America"

My grandmother said nothing, just looked up from her baking and sniffed.

I thought the reaction was a bit strange and, although I was dying to tell her what the man had said, I didn't. Oddly enough, neither did my aunt. There followed an awkward silence.

Then the penny dropped. "Tom Kelly," I thought, that's the name in Mammy's book.

I forgot all about it when my friend Helen called at the door for me.

"Are you coming out to have fun. The gypsies are down the lane coming from the Puck Fair. Come on and we'll watch them. Come on, girl, the lane is full of caravans."

I didn't dare tell my grandmother where I was headed.

"Goodbye Nana," I called out innocently, "I'm going down to Helen's house to play."

And off the pair of us headed for the lane.

There I was introduced for the first time to the joys of breastfeeding. The woman didn't seem to mind her audience as she sat on the steps of a caravan, breastfeeding her chubby baby.

I stood there silently with my mouth hanging open. Then I whispered to my friend: "Why is that baby eating his mother, why is she letting him?"

The mother just smiled at us as her baby gobbled her with great smacking noises. Then Helen and I ran up the lane.

I had forgotten all about Tom Kelly.

When I got back home from my holidays, I told my mother about the encounter. She seemed pleased, but still did not tell me who "Tom Kelly" was.

Some years later when "Mammy" had become "Mom", I asked the same old question: "Mom, who is Tom Kelly?"

At long last, I got an answer.

"Well, Tom Kelly was my first boyfriend, I suppose you might say, my first love."

Shyly she turned away and busied herself baking scones, a daily task in our house.

"Tell me about him, Mom? And tell me what his name is doing on your book?"

She put the tray of scones into the oven. I helped her clear up. Then she sat down opposite me and told me her story.

"It was all so long ago - the early twenties. This country was in a state of turmoil. It breaks my heart when I think of all that went on. At that time we were so passionate about our beloved Ireland. Tom was a very brave young man, very active in the I.R.A. Things were going from bad to worse and then Tom, like so many others, was 'on the run.' He stayed in safe houses and, as there was little or no communication, things became very difficult for us.

"I never knew when or where we would meet. Out of the blue he would appear and then disappear just as quickly. Then disaster struck. Tom was arrested and sent to jail. As you can imagine, I was devastated."

My mother sighed deeply.

"But all of us, in our own way, did our bit. We raised funds for the I.R.A. by organising concerts in small towns all over Kerry."

As she spoke, she lifted her head and announced proudly: "I sang 'The Tri-coloured Ribbon' at concerts when it was dangerous to sing it. But, dear God, I missed Tom sorely. We were kindred spirits and wrote to each other every week. I sent him small gifts of books, cigarettes and useful items of clothing.

"As I had plenty of time while Tom was in jail, I set myself the task of reading my new book 'Works of William Shakespeare.' It took me ages to finish it.

"When I wrote and told Tom this, I offered to lend the book to him. He promised to take great care of it. I gladly sent it to him. I thought it might cheer him up as his letters had become a bit gloomy for a while past. I liked the idea of Tom turning the same pages I had turned and reading the same words I had read. I felt it might bring us a little bit closer."

Again she sighed and then continued: "I was a hopeless romantic in those days. After spending two long weary years in jail, word came that Tom was being released. I was overjoyed and could not wait to meet him again. I was puzzled when I heard that he had been home for three days and had not called up to our house-puzzled and a bit upset.

"When he did call and I opened the door to him, he held out his hand to me. I put my arms around him and hugged him. I was crying but so happy to see him. Tom held me at arm's length. I brought him into our little sitting-room and we sat down. I looked at him. He had not changed much, he was a bit thinner but it was the look in his eyes, the only way I could describe it, his eyes looked half dead in his head. He was so cold to me, totally unlike the Tom I had known, he was more like a stranger. He never even attempted to kiss me nor I him. I think I knew then that it was over."

"But, Mom, what did you do but love and support him for the two years?"

"I know, love, but remember nobody talked about depression in those days and jail had an awful effect on him."

My Mam's eyes filled up and I held her hand.

She continued: "We met a few times afterwards, but he felt all their sacrifices had been in vain. There were no jobs for the Sinn Feiners. By now I had a good job and he had nothing. So, at his instigation, we parted company. I was heart-broken. About two weeks later, Tom called to my house and returned my book. He would not come in. That was the last time I spoke to him. I cried myself to sleep that night.

"Now and then I would bump into him on the street. He would just nod and keep on walking while my breaking heart would thump and I would feel myself getting weak at the knees. Then someone told me Tom had gone to America. He never said goodbye."

My mother sat there twisting her wedding ring around her finger.

"I'd say those scones are done by now. Will you take them out for me, love?"

After what seemed like ages, I asked my mother: "Mam, when did you meet Dad?"

She smiled at me. "You're a terrible one for asking questions. Well, after Tom went away I did, of course, meet other boys and went out with one or two. But to tell the truth, I had a horror of them. You see, I couldn't forget Tom. He had a very special place in my heart."

"But how did you meet Dad?"

"Well, I began to pray that I would find a boy I could love. Marriage was expected of a girl at that time and I was aware of that. But when I met him first he was introduced to me as Kathleen O'Connor's boy. But that romance didn't last too long. Then he asked me out. When I got to know him, I thought he was the most gentle and loving fellow, for a country boy. Soon I fell in love with him."

My Dad and Mam were like chalk and cheese. She was into the arts and was an avid reader all her life. My father loved sport, the newspapers, Zane Grey and a weekly magazine called "Everybody." He loved children, animals and nature.

He was never happier than when he was in the garden, working away and stopping to listen to the birds. He has a granddaughter who feels exactly the same. He loved simple songs that told a story. He loved Stephen Foster's music and sang us to sleep with his old favourites when we were little.

My mother was more complex. She had a beautiful operatic voice, but never sang us to sleep as every song had to be performed. She loved light operas and had principal parts in The Gondoliers, The Mikado and The Pirates of Penzance.

One thing we were always sure of was the love between our parents. At a time when most Irish people were not demonstrative, our family was. My father kissed my mother and all of us when he left for work in the morning and when he returned, also before we went to bed. Our friends thought we were a bit weird.

Perhaps we were. But our family was happy.

One morning when my parents were well in their seventies, I got a phone call from my mother. She sounded a bit excited.

"I had the most amazing dream last night."

"About what, Mam?"

"I dreamt I was young and single and walking along arm-in-arm with Tom Kelly, as we always had. We were so happy and so much in love. It was wonderful and so real.

"Then your Dad woke me up. I stared at him and wondered who was this old man in the bed beside me. I was still in that happy dreamlike state. Then I was really awake and feeling so guilty. But I did not tell your Dad about my dream. Ever since I've been going around the house with a smile on my face. Am I going daft?"

A week or so later, my Mam phoned me again. "You're not going to believe this. Last night I was reading 'The Kerryman' and what did I read: 'The death took place last week in New York of Thomas Kelly.' They gave details of his family and it definitely was Tom.

"Now tell me, what do you make of that dream I had last week?"

What indeed?

THE WINTER CHERRY

BY BERNADETTE CARROLL,
Navan, Co. Meath

When you're only six-years-old, it can be difficult to understand the reactions of adults

" WHY ARE YOU CRYING, GRANNY? You should be happy, you got a present!" It was Christmas week in the early 1960s. We'd just had an exciting event, an unexpected caller.

A florist from the town had delivered a plant, a winter cherry, splendid in its ornate container. Its vibrant red berries lit up our little kitchen on that dull winter day. The accompanying note was from my uncle Nicky in Brisbane.

I remember Granny, frail and white-haired, still wearing the widow's black after twenty-six years. She was holding the winter cherry, her eyes wet with silent tears.

It was 1938 when my uncle, my granny's first-born, left for Australia, a twenty-four-year-old, ready for adventure. Already a widow, she kissed him good-bye outside the thatched farmhouse, as he embarked on his journey, one that would take several weeks.

Over the long years, there were letters and photos of his new family, children posing in shorts on scorching beaches, a world away from the long, winding lane that the postman trudged along, carrying the precious packages.

When the thatched roof started to decay and the mud walls to crumble, Granny came to live with us in our slate-roofed roadside cottage. She would sit by the open fire, with her prayer book, packed with novenas and memoriam cards, gaining comfort from her faith.

Uncle Nicky came home for the first and only time in the early 70s, a grey-haired man of fifty-eight. Granny was not there to greet him, she was resting under the yew trees in the nearby small, hilly graveyard.

At Christmas time, as I wander around the shopping malls and the garden centres, I sometimes come across the winter cherry, and think of her. No phones, no emails, no skype, no cheap flights condensing six weeks into twenty-four hours. I hope that she is with her son now, "where every tear will be wiped away."

"Why are you crying, Granny? You should be happy, you got a present!"

Life is very simple when you're a six-year-old.

THE TAILOR'S TWIST

BY LIAM GAUL,
Wexford town

*A tailor experiences a full measure of joys and sorrows in a journey
that takes him from rags to riches and back to rags again*

IT WAS A COLD December evening just before Christmas. The light was fading, giving the leafless trees an eerie effect as they stood with bare arms stretching skywards towards a winter moon which was masked from time to time by scurrying clouds. A lone figure was wending his way along a silent country road carrying a large bag which contained the tools of his trade and a few belongings.

He was a journeyman tailor whose life in latter years seemed to have been spent tramping the highways and byways of Ireland in the hope of plying his ancient craft. It wasn't always the case. Misfortune had changed the life of Johnny Maloney, a frail man fast approaching his three score and ten years. Like many tailors, Johnny had never enjoyed good health as tailoring was a sedentary craft, sitting cross-legged on a bench or, most times, on a small piece of timber laid on the floor sewing, day in, day out.

As a young man, Johnny served his apprenticeship with a neighbouring tailor learning his trade with very little pay for his efforts. The hours were long, working from early light to late evening crouched over a garment and inserting endless rows of stitching, or so it seemed to the young lad.

His own father, also a tailor, thought it best to send his son to someone else to learn his craft. His training complete, the young Maloney set out from his village in the Gaelic- speaking area of County Waterford in the hope of making his fortune in the bustling metropolis of London. Lady luck smiled on him for he was successful in securing a job in the heart of tailoring - Savile Row.

His prayers and pleas to Saint Homobonus, the patron saint of tailors, had been answered at last. His early training at home stood him in good stead, for soon his talent for precise workmanship and attention to detail brought well-earned promotion and, of course, an increase in his wages.

It was now Johnny Maloney, Bespoke Tailor, a title which denoted that he could hand-make garments or suits completely original and unique to each customer. His soft Irish brogue and gentle manner brought many clients to his employer's tailor's shop asking for the Irishman to make their clothes. As time passed, it was Johnny who measured, fitted and made clothes for some of the most famous in the land from judges, lawyers, politicians and even royalty, to their utter satisfaction.

One trait this Irish tailor had was to put a penny piece in one of the coat pockets for every suit he completed, for luck. It was an old tradition to handsel the new garment by putting a coin in the pocket so that the wearer would never be short or run out of money. The strange thing was none of his clients ever commented or questioned this odd practise, much to Johnny's amazement. Coming from the Deise, a place steeped in ancient custom and lore, this handselling of a new garment was second nature.

The years passed quickly in the hustle and bustle of London and Johnny Maloney's reputation as a creative artist in the tailoring world grew, and, following many promptings from clients, he decided the time had come to branch out with his own business. He bade farewell to Sammy Bloomberg, his friendly and generous Jewish employer and took a premises further along Savile Row. A whole new beginning for the young tailor began some days later when he turned the key to open his very own sartorial emporium.

The shop front looked well, painted in emerald green with gold lettering proudly proclaiming - The Tailor's Twist, proprietor John Maloney, Master Tailor. The shop name seemed appropriate as tailor's twist was the very strong sewing thread for stitching around the edges of button holes and for general hand-sewing throughout a garment.

Johnny remembered it was also the name of a very fine hornpipe tune played by a local uilleann piper from Ring. Well, customers seemed to just flow in through the tailor's shop and very soon Johnny had to employ extra tailors to cope with the influx of work.

One day a very tall refined gentleman came in seeking the owner's advice on the supply of a suitable horse-riding habit for a prince of the realm. This meant a visit to Windsor Castle and a meeting with his royal client to take measurements and to arrange for further visits for a 'try-on' of the new clothes.

These visits became very regular as further orders came from the royal household, finally culminating in a Royal Warrant which Johnny proudly displayed on the facade of his shop. An tailíur beag ó na Déise had really arrived.

The Tailor's Twist made Johnny Maloney an extremely wealthy man, and thoughts of returning home to Ireland became uppermost in his mind so that he could set up again in his own native place. Setting himself a date to be home for St. Patrick's Day the following year, Johnny informed his many clients and closed his shop to the dismay and disappointment of many.

When he finally turned the key to lock his premises for the last time, he called in to see Mr. Bloomberg, now a very old man, before heading for Paddington Station on the first leg of his return journey to Sliabh Geal gCua. The words of Pádraig Ó Míléadha song were ringing in his head:

If I were there with my people,
On the green-clad hills,
 Warmed by the heat of the sun,
In a bright, cloudless sky,
Or if I were there on a starry night,
As dew falls on the grass,
Oh radiant mount Cua,
That would be wealth beyond compare.

On landing at Rosslare Harbour, it was only a short journey to County Waterford and home

Following a few days meeting and greeting family and friends, Johnny thought it time to find a premises in which to open his Tailor's Twist. A fine shop on Dungarvan's Main Street was available and, with some refurbishment and fresh paint work, he had a grand opening for Easter. Customers flocked in, all looking for the latest in suits, sport coats and overcoats, all made to measure.

He increased his in-house tailoring staff to four and outsourced repairs, alterations and 'turns' to local seamstresses and older tailors who preferred to work at home to try to cope with the massive workload. Thoughts of diversification came about by extending his shop to cater for gent's accessories such as shirts, ties and high-class shoes. An advertisement in the Munster Express brought a series of interviews and, after some deliberation, a female assistant was hired in the outfitting department of the shop.

Mary O'Connor was a very able assistant and a good sales lady with a pleasing smile and friendly demeanour. She and Johnny hit it off very well and seemed as if they had known each other for years.

Mary was unmarried and lived on the edge of town with her widowed mother. By this time, Maloney had learned to drive and had a shiny new Austin A30 motorcar, the envy of the business community. Often of a rainy evening at close of business, Johnny would willingly give Mary O'Connor a lift home, and soon a relationship blossomed between the two of them.

Johnny Maloney was elated as he had gone fifty years of age and never had the inclination to get married. Love found a way and, within six months, Johnny had proposed and was accepted. Wedding plans were set in train and, before Lent the following year, Johnny and Mary were married in the local church to the delight of the widow O'Connor and the Maloney family.

Happiness reigned. Mary was befriended by many of her new

neighbours as her mother and herself had come to live over the shop with Johnny since their marriage. The couple proved to be extremely popular in their community and were in attendance at the many local functions held in the town and beyond.

In early November, they travelled to their neighbouring County Wexford as guests at a society wedding and decided to travel home late that night, much against the wishes of their hosts as the weather had turned rather wintery. In mid-journey, snow began to fall and visibility became difficult. Driving conditions were hazardous.

Johnny knew they were not far from home and increased his speed somewhat as the falling snow had eased. Earlier wet roads had frozen and, as the Maloney's car rounded a dangerous bend, it skidded on an icy patch. Try as he might, Johnny couldn't keep control of the vehicle as it careered into a gripe and hit the ditch.

They were discovered the next morning by a farmer passing the road on his tractor. Some days later, Johnny woke up in hospital battered and bruised but alive. Later, the hospital chaplain entered the ward accompanied by Mary's mother and broke the sad news that Mary had not survived the terrible accident.

When he was finally released from hospital weeks later, Johnny Maloney's world had fallen apart for Mrs. O'Connor had suffered a sudden heart attack and died. All the things he had worked for over the years had come to nothing. Left with a limp from his injuries, Johnny spent most of his time and his money in a local public house, hoping that the whiskey would dull the pain of his huge losses.

His business suffered and soon his bank balance diminished, his customers were gone and, eventually, the For Sale sign went up in The Tailor's Twist shop window. Johnny had kept the tools of his trade, a cutting shears, scissors, needles, threads, thimbles, marking chalk, tape measure and the pressing iron known as the 'goose'.

There was nothing for it but to take to the roads and try to eke out a living as a journeyman tailor. There was many a hungry day and cold sleepless night spent in draughty barns and outhouses which were the only source of shelter for the beleaguered tailor. Unlike many of his customers, his own clothes were threadbare and offered little protection against the chill winter winds and rain.

He could see the outline of the fine country mansion silhouetted against the moonlit sky and, as he drew nearer, a warm glow of light emanated from the large drawing room windows. A knock on the well-polished brass door knocker brought a young servant girl to enquire as to his wants. On hearing the conversation, a tall silver-haired gentleman came down the hall and, looking at Johnny, cordially invited him into his house, much to the dismay of the ragged, weather-beaten tailor.

Casting a quizzical eye on the tailor, the gentleman asked if he was the tailor from The Tailor's Twist in London. A nod from Johnny and the gentleman moved across the fine drawing room to open a drawer in an ornately-carved rosewood chiffonier. After a moment, he stood in front of Johnny. In his hand was an English penny piece. The tailor wiped tears from his eyes as he gazed on the handsel penny he had placed in the coat pocket of this man's jacket many years ago.

The gentleman, being of Irish descent, knew the significance of the coin and explained to Johnny the success and wealth it had brought him, culminating in his being ennobledfor his services to the realm. On retirement to Ireland, he had bought the mansion and the surrounding lands which were farmed by his many tenants and provided welcome employment in the area.

The gentleman indicated that there was ample work for a tailor on the estate and surrounding countryside and village. Much to Johnny's delight, he offered him a place to stay and set up his tailoring workshop. Johnny's luck had changed and the Tailor's Twist was about to be revived once again.

WATCHING WITH MOTHER

By Paul McLaughlin,
Marmount Gardens, Belfast

Mother had received a telegram from the King announcing the death of my father in France, and she kept it wrapped as tightly as a pound note being saved for a rainy day

WHEN GRANNY took sick, Aunt Maria switched off the television set that had all but replaced the piano as the main focal point of our living room. It remained sad and silent for many weeks, although to my confusion, the wireless, with its huge amplified face, was taken down and dusted and tuned almost immediately to the Home Service.

Maria called the television a "foolish and frivolous thing that has no place in a sick house" and such words brooked no argument.

Granda, whose long, artistic fingers had tickled the ivories, as he called them, with tunes as varied as the Blue Danube and Boolavogue, had tripped in front of a tram on the eve of his 60th birthday and the key to the piano lid had been taken from his tattered waistcoat pocket and turned decisively in its lock.

It had stood, locked, for more than three years, hiding its rows of black and white teeth, before the big eye of the television cast its blue, flickering, hypnotic gaze across the interior of our prefab.

The light had gone out now, slowly at first until a big white dot had centred itself on screen, then suddenly with a click that had a note of finality, Valentine Dyall's "Frankenstein voice" and the sea-shanty rhythm of the shipping forecast had replaced "Watch with Mother."

Aunt Maria dabbed her eyes a lot more now, speaking in whispers that still sounded like her customary orders, while Mother, her chin on permanent jut, said I must be "a brave wee soldier."

"Granny isn't well and we need you to be the man of the house now", she said, patting my head and arranging my hair at the same time.

I don't remember there ever being a man in our house, apart from Paddy, the bread server, and Mister Dunn, who did odd jobs and ate all the bap when he'd finished them. And I couldn't think why a man was needed so much just because Granny was being taken into hospital. But, soldiers obey orders they don't understand and Mother knew best, as Granny always said.

I was nine years old and stood to attention and saluted badly when I saw either of the two new matriarchs of the house. I had seen soldiers on television and I knew the drill. Neither woman had acknowledged my military addresses, however. Women were too busy cooking and cleaning and then making themselves pretty, even on the TV, to see the importance of such things.

Aunt Maria was in her early thirties then and widowed since 1941 when her husband Harry had suffered a fatal heart attack during the second great blitz of the city. He had suffered, the doctors had said, for only a few seconds, but Maria's suffering had been loud and long-lasting and, unfortunately, to my mind at least, never-ending if she was within earshot of another human being.

She moaned during the day to anyone who would listen and sobbed at night when the wireless had been turned off and Granny's incessant prayers had come to an end and her snoring permeated the paper-thin walls of the bungalow.

But, that was Aunt Maria. She had declared Harry a war hero, refused to join in the happy throng that had conga-ed snakelike to the city hall on VE night and retreated to the little shrine in her heart where he would be remembered, endearingly and vociferously, always.

Mother was no stranger to loss and hurt either. She had

172

received a telegram from the King that had announced the departure of my father as he had invaded France, showing "great gallantry and fortitude." She kept the official note in her handbag wrapped as tightly as a pound note being saved for a rainy day. And the sun had not shone on her head since.

But her pain was the slow, silent drip of a tear that refuses to fall, at least in public. She talked of the sacrifice of countless millions, of the little children who had lost their lives and their footholds in the future and the holy gift of faith that held us all together. I thought of plasticine and how to make an elephant's head like the one I had seen on Picture Book.

So it was that I, Denis, "Donnelly", after my Mother's people, Moreland, newly- acquainted with the wonders of the British Broadcasting Corporation in 1953, was left a year later staring at an empty screen and a reflection that showed a boy's focussed eyes and an empty house that, somehow, seemed ready to burst.

School at St Martha's Primary took up almost all of my spare time that April as the Easter test came and went and my class results went up and down like the wee, plastic diver I controlled by screwing and unscrewing the top of a lemonade bottle filled with water.

Our teacher, Mister Green, who normally twisted boys by the locks of their pre-adolescent sideburns, had been abnormally understanding, saying in a soft voice that I was inconsistent and needed to concentrate. I nodded in agreement, despite not knowing what he was talking about while, tentatively, fingering the right, razored edge of my short back and sides.

My two best friends at St Martha's, who both had fathers with belts that threatened bruises and abrasions on occasions, told me that I didn't know how lucky I was to be an orphan or even half an orphan.

Mickey and Brian would have given anything, they said, to have had an empty armchair at their firesides. But they didn't live in our house.

Granny was very sick the first time that I was allowed into the City Hospital for an afternoon visit. She lay on her back in the main ward, very pale and sleeping despite the clatter and din of dozens of other visitors, some with funny, country accents, who chattered and chewed and chomped their way through 45 minutes until a large handbell had called them to disperse.

There had been kissing and hugging, a few hankies and a lot of tears at their departure. Aunt Maria squeezed Granny's hand and tried to fit her fist into her eye sockets, while sniffling loudly. Mother said simply, "Cheerio Mammy, we'll see you this evening."

I said nothing and waited to be frogmarched out of a building that had a very queer smell masking others that I recognised, but couldn't mention. At least, not in front of Mother.

"Missus Dunne will mind you tonight, while we go to see Granny at the hospital, Denis," said Mother, ladling out stew from the big saucepan;

"So, be on your best behaviour until we get home."

"Yes, Mammy", I said automatically, thinking of Missus Dunn's moustache and imagining her as one of the three musketeers I had seen at the Broadway picture house. She would not have been out of place, I thought, apart from the snuff-stained pinafore, because she wore her hair long and could ride a bike faster than anyone in our street.

And bikes were just like horses, weren't they? Although the nearest I had come to a horse, apart from on television and the cinema, was to rein the shaft of Granny's floor brush between my legs as I galloped to Coleman's shop on the far corner for the early Belfast Telegraph every afternoon.

Today, I had returned, newspaper in one hand, my trusty steed in the other. As I was stabling it in the broom cupboard off the scullery, I watched, out of the corner of my eye, as Mother and Aunt Maria sipped tea, heads almost touching in a lacework of whispers, at the pull-down table.

They were dressed in top coats and head scarves, my Mother's a flimsy bright yellow that matched, she said, the dark brown of her overcoat, while Aunt Maria wore the black mantilla that matched her mood.

"Mammy?" I asked, waiting to win her full attention.

"Mam-my" and the second syllable was like a petulant plea.

"I have a shilling and ninepence in Mister Coleman's club", and I proffered the savings' card evidence for both to see.

"Can I buy something for Granny to make her better?"

Aunt Maria spoke first as usual: "Your Granny is very sick, Denis, and there's nothing Mister Coleman has that will make her better."

I knew Beechams' Powders could cure anything, but I said nothing. Mister Dunn swore by them, swearing out loud when Mother and Maria weren't around and telling me that all men swear to show that they're proper men. But Mister Dunn also spat and broke wind for the same reason.

"Go on, Denis, put the card away," said Mother softly, the way she used to before Granny went away.

"Go and switch on the television and we'll watch 'Bill and Ben' before we go to see our Mother."

THE VISITATION

BY NORA BRENNAN,
Glendine Heights, Kilkenny

*I was mesmerised: the sight of the three pale-faced nuns in long veils
was the nearest I had ever seen of the Blessed Virgin*

IT WAS A SUMMER afternoon in 1971 and I was walking
a reek of hay in the shed. My father turned the tractor into
the haggard and reversed the buck-rake with the next hay
cock for my brothers to pitch.

"You have to go in," he shouted. "The visitors are here."
My two sisters and I scampered down the steep ladder, wisps
of hay in our hair and tattered clothes. Inside the house, the
kitchen was deserted. We followed the murmur to the parlour
where our mother sat with three nuns robed in blue and white.
One was my aunt and I recognised her from the photograph
which had been taken during her novitiate and which hung on
the wall in our dining room.

"What sweet little darlings we have here," she said as we
walked in. My mother introduced us and I waited my turn to
shake hands. I was mesmerised: the sight of the three pale-faced
nuns in long veils was the nearest I had ever seen of the Blessed
Virgin.

"You're great girls to be helping your Daddy bring in the
hay," my aunt said. We sat on the sofa by the far window
where lace drapes swayed gently in the breeze. The silver tray
and gold-rimmed drinking glasses had already been polished
and my sister served fizzy orange and a plate of biscuits. I
was banking on the left-overs but, as the afternoon wore on,
I watched glasses empty and the marshmallow creams, my
favourite, disappear.

The conversation ranged from life in Vietnam to the work of the nuns. My mother was using a language I had never heard before. "Oh goodness!" and "gosh!" she kept saying when they spoke about monsoon climates and young girls who got into trouble wandering the streets in the night.

I couldn't understand the details, but when they chatted about classes in embroidery and needlework, I wanted to know more. It sounded like a far better option than walking the hay.I looked at the tight bands around their faces, the way they were sealed around the edges like the plastic face of my pink doll. How they managed to work in the sweltering heat and keep their garments so spotless, I did not know.

"We'll go and see how Mike and the boys are doing," my aunt said as the afternoon wore on.

I ran out to the haggard to call them in. By the time we got to the front of the house, the party had floated from the parlour to the sunshine and flowers in the lawn.

"God save you," my father said taking off his hat and extending his hand.

"Hello Mike. You're doing great work I heard. And these two fine young men."She reached out to my two lanky-legged brothers. There were more introductions before one of my brothers disappeared for the large black-eyed camera box and my sisters and I changed into our good clothes.

We lined up with a border of snapdragons and rockets by our feet. Photographs were taken as we strolled around the garden and house – the home of my aunt before she joined the religious order at sixteen years of age.

Tea was a more elaborate affair than normal.The silver cutlery had been freshly polished, fine bone china sparkled and my mother had a reserve of sliced cooked ham and tomatoes. The table was laden with freshly-baked brown bread and apple tart. I listened intently to conversations about farmers up to their knees in water as they planted rice; the way rice was eaten morning, noon and night, and how the nuns never saw brown bread since they left the shores of Ireland.

When the time came to say goodbye, my aunt reached deep

into the folds of her habit and took out what seemed like an endless supply of gifts. There were holy pictures for each of us, rosary beads and scapulars for my parents and handkerchiefs with our initials embroidered on them.

That visit was the first of many as rules about travel relaxed in religious orders. My aunt moved to Thailand in 1977, having narrowly escaped during the fall of South Vietnam to the communists in 1975. Recently, my siblings and I gathered to wish her a happy 93rd birthday.

Her face beamed onto the centre of the computer screen as she greeted us from her community in the north east of Thailand. Dressed in pale blue and white, she looked radiant. We blew out candles, held the cake within reach of a webcam and sang Happy Birthday. She, with unfailing wit and wisdom, marvelled at technology and wondered what it would offer us ten years from now.

Short story

WINNER TAKES ALL

BY WILLIAM CROWE,
Caherdavin, Limerick

*Overnight, Paudie was everybody's best friend as they became
convinced he had won the lottery, but Paudie knew that his newly-
acquired status would not last*

P AUDIE CROFT lived alone on the outskirts of Lackin
Village. Paudie was a man of middle-age, living on a
disability allowance. When asked about the nature of his
disability he always replied: "I have a bit of an auld limp." His
existence, though frugal, was one of contentment, happy to live
a leisurely and carefree life among the people and environment
of Lackin.

His philosophical outlook was to live life as it came. He
had no relations nearby to support or trouble him. He seldom
travelled and somebody once remarked that if a world war
started up in the next parish it would not affect him in the
slightest. In spite of his easygoing and sheltered existence,
however, he was well read and nobody's fool.

Life in Lackin wasn't exactly a hive of activity in any sense
and nothing seemed to disturb its laid-back and tranquil way
of life. But change, when it does come, often comes quickly. So
it was on a bright summer's morning when the news broke that
the winning ticket for the previous night's National Lottery
Draw had been sold in the local supermarket. Immediately
the sleepy village came to life and a sense of euphoria took
hold of the people. Nothing like this had ever happened
before. Excitement was quickly followed by rumour and
speculation as to who the lucky winner of the two million Euro
prize might be.

179

Due to the geographical location of Lackin on the road to nowhere with little passing traffic, it became widely believed that the winner was most likely a local. But who? That was the question! The supermarket boss couldn't possibly remember all those who had purchased tickets. A few days elapsed with no clue as to who had won the fortune. If it was a local man or woman, he or she was keeping very quiet about it.

Curiosity was rampant, and so the watch began. The entire population went on high alert and neighbour kept close eye on neighbour for any sign of affluence or spending beyond the normal. Days went by without a single pointer emerging as to the identity of the new millionaire, and people settled in for what many now suspected would be a long wait. But to their great relief, a suspect soon emerged.

Just over a week had passed since the exciting news of the lottery win had hit the public when Paudie Croft took the early train to Dublin. That in itself was news, as Paudie very seldom travelled anywhere. But when he arrived back home later the same afternoon resplendent in a smashing new suit, matching shirt and tie, and patent leather shoes, parish eyes dilated and wise heads nodded knowingly. Like the Canadian Mounties, they had their man. It only remained now for Paudie to come clean but, to their great surprise, he remained silent. An affable and talkative man, he wasn't thought of as one who would harbour secrets.

Money, unlike many other commodities, is of interest to everybody and so the task of prising a confession out of Paudie began in earnest. While nobody was willing to put the question directly, since a man is entitled to his privacy, all sorts of strategies and subterfuges were resorted to.

The matter absorbed the attention of the entire community and curiosity was at fever pitch. Days went by and still no word from Paudie. Still, the belief persisted, and it wasn't long before news of his reputed good fortune spread to a much wider audience.

Subsequent days saw Paudie's incoming mail ballooning from the occasional letter to double digit figures. Offers of great

HGHLY COMMENDED

investment opportunities, on most of which he was informed
that he was being given first refusal, came from several financial
institutions; requests from numerous charities requesting
donations for domestic and overseas projects poured in, and
sporting clubs and organisations asked for help for anything
from new dressing rooms to line-marking equipment.

The begging letters from individuals and families interested
him most of all. While some were undoubtedly genuine pleas
for help, he felt the majority came from confidence tricksters
and chancers. He had to admire the ingenuity and inventiveness
of the latter. If they applied their imaginative skills to more
worthwhile and productive causes, he felt they could be very
successful.

The resident Bank Manager, who had never previously
noticed him, now, armed with a broad smile, saluted him
heartily by name. The local tuppence-halfpenny looking down
on tuppence brigade came out in force and tacitly admitted
him to their august circle. Free drinks abounded in the local
pub, some offered in genuine celebration of his huge win, while
others came in the form of an investment, with a view to a
good return when Paudie declared his millionaire status and
began to share his good fortune.

Overnight, he became everybody's best friend and was
secretly enjoying his celebrity status. But he was well aware
of the reason for this and knew it wouldn't last. Outwardly,
he didn't alter one iota of his normal lifestyle and remained
as calm and composed as he had always been. He had the
outside walls and gate of his compact dwelling painted and
his lawnmower serviced, but other than that he displayed no
evidence of increased spending power or affluence.

A month passed and still no breakthrough. While it was not
unknown for a big money winner to bide his time and make an
unhurried decision on what was best for him in the long term,
still the urge to splash out like there was no tomorrow must be
a huge temptation in such circumstances. It was only human
after all.

While many were still convinced of Paudie's good fortune,

181

others began to doubt. Gradually, his letter-box became less busy, investment invitations and requests for donations dwindled to a trickle, the Bank Manager's broad smile became less broad and the supply of free drinks dried up. Rory Houlin expressed the view that even if he had won the money he wouldn't have a clue how to manage it. "Once a pauper, always a pauper," he stated in an attempt at the ultimate put-down.

Paudie carried on as if he didn't notice that the favourable wind blowing in his direction had shifted. His conduct and demeanour were so natural for him that they gave no indication as to whether he was or was not a wealthy man.

Change, when it comes, often comes quickly. And so it transpired in the case of Paudie's reputed lottery win. A woman from the parish next to Lackin, having bided her time and secured the future of her massive windfall, went public. She also visited the Lackin supermarket in the presence of the local Press and presented the owner with a cheque as a gesture of thanksgiving for having been sold the winning ticket there.

This removed any doubts that may still have lingered in the minds of the people of Lackin. Emotion ran high – some residents were angry and felt cheated at what they considered Paudie's duplicity, others took it in their stride with many pretending they never believed the story anyway. Still others saw the funny side of it. Paudie, for his part, went to ground, allowing for a cooling off period before facing the inevitable inquisition.

When he did appear in the local pub a week later, he was immediately surrounded by a group of up to twenty customers. He was reprimanded, scolded, teased, congratulated and praised for his recent performance. In his defence, Paudie pointed out that he had never claimed to have won the two million Euro, he had simply never denied it.

"A lie of omission so," sneered one customer.

"Well, not exactly," Paudie explained. "True, I didn't win the National Lottery, but my brother in Dublin entered my name in the lottery draw run by his local GAA Club and I won five hundred euro."

Life in Lackin returned to normal and Paudie continued to live quietly as he had always done. But he admitted to himself that his brief claim to fame had been nice while it lasted.

THE COTTAGE

By Martina Phelan,
Douglas Road, Cork.

*Grainne just couldn't envisage leaving Chicago to live in a cottage
down a long lane with no street lights, no paths, no neighbours.
This was her father's dream, not hers.*

" I DON'T KNOW what I'm looking at," said Grainne. "I
don't know what you want me to say." She was looking
at a pile of stones – rocks really. Some were still in the
shape of the old stone walls, more had tumbled down into
heaps and were covered over with ivy. Sure, she could see that
it used to be "The Cottage", but what was it now?

"The future, me darling," said her father in his fake Oirish
accent. He stood at the old door jamb and gestured for his
daughter to follow.

"Looks more like the past to me, Father," she quipped as she
stepped over the rubble and after him into the old house. There
was hardly a room here, it was entirely open to the sky, with
the walls crumbled down to waist height.

"This was the kitchen, here is the window, and this is where
the table would have been. Look at the hearth, it's hardly been
touched by time. I can remember my aunt Maggie sitting over
here drinking her tea and shouting at the cat. I can picture her
as though it was last year, not fifty years ago."

And indeed, the hearth was still intact, as high as her
shoulders, but piled high with old ashes, topped by the
remnants of years of birds' nests, all tumbling down onto the
broken flagstones.

"And the roof, Daddy? Now where would that have been?"
She moved to the middle of the room. She hugged the sycamore

tree growing up from the centre of the floor and twirled around it as she looked upward. There was nothing left that the sycamore had not swept away as it had quietly reached for the grey sky.

"But look at how high the ceiling would have been," her father protested as he pointed out the remaining rafters to the left and to the right of the kitchen. "Isn't that something else? What would your friend think of that, huh? Him and his 'light and space, light and space'."

Actually, she thought, this was as far as one could get from her boyfriend's idea of a good design. When she met him first, the day she interviewed for a position in his firm, she had thought how intelligent he had sounded. After a year of listening to the same opinions, she wondered if the only lectures he had attended were: Lecture 1 – The importance of light and space, and Lecture 2 – Form follows function. Now go forth and draw.

But she didn't want him in the conversation or in her mind so she just shrugged and said: "Oh yeah, he'd love a pile of falling down stones all right," and laughed.

They moved left into the upper room. Here the rafters clung on to position and the roof was almost intact. The room was pitch dark, the one small window clouded with dirt. She stumbled going over the step and putting her hands out to catch herself, felt the cold of the walls.

Her father, ahead of her, leaned into the deep window to pull at the old window frame. It gave a little, letting in a couple of inches of sunlight. The room was empty - no furniture, no trees, just dark and dust. She allowed her fingers to stay pressed against the cold stone. She thought of the generations of people who had lived here, who had built this house, been proud of this house, thought it plenty big enough; women who had scrubbed and scoured, men who had painted and patched. And then fifty years left to the elements, and the birds and trees - the wind and rain must have laughed as they took it over.

Back they went through the open space of the kitchen to the lower room. This was another small, dark bedroom, one deep window with its glass broken and the ivy stretching in. This room had the shape of a bed in it. She shivered at the sight of this old metal bed still made up with a damp, rotten cover. She imagined the ghosts of old women, all pushing each other to roll over and give a little room.

"Let's get out of here," she said. "It's warmer outside in the rain."

As they left the cottage, her father stooped to pull at something half-hidden in the earth. It was a tea cup, the blue willow pattern clear under the dust.

"I'll give you a cup of tea in that cup the next time you are here, just you see, kid."

He laughed at her wrinkling her nose at all this dust and dirt. How did he raise this city girl, he wondered, and not for the first time.

They returned to the farmhouse to warm up. It was really all a joke as far as Grainne could see. The death of her mother had left him half mad and fully free and the money was all going on this pipe-dream. What did he know of farming and what did he really know of Ireland, that cold, wet place he remembered from boyhood? But here he was, a few cows, a horse, the two-storey farmhouse and the cottage down the lane.

They joked in Tiffcrum that he was just another yank coming home to die, but he was far too young for that. He was coming home to live! She hadn't seen him so happy since, well, since they were all together. In his former life as an art teacher in Chicago, she couldn't ever remember him in the garden. But now he was busy with his land, making places, buying animals, meeting his neighbours, pestering his cousins no doubt. But this cottage? What was the point?

"I'm going to bring it back to its former self. For a start, I'll begin with the walls in the living room, and the roof will be no trouble to me. Maybe I'll even manage to save some of the flagstones. And then we'll see, maybe I'll even bring it into the 21st century. I could wire it and plumb it, put in a bathroom of course. I'll bring in some help and get it all cosy and warm. And then when you come over to visit, you'll have your own place to stay. Who knows, maybe you'll fall in love with this place and make it your own. After all, is leor don dreoilin a nead."

She gave him a warning look and he quickly explained. "The nest is enough for a wren, Grainne. A place like this would be a fine home if your heart was here."

Well, she couldn't envisage it - down this long lane in the dark night, with no street lights, no paths, no neighbours. Not for her. And anyway, she would be lucky to make it over every couple of years. She could just stay with him. Her job gave her ten days' vacation a year, not enough to need her own Irish cottage. Just enough time, this time, for a tour of South Armagh, its low mountains, its sharp wind and its endless cups of tea.

And soon, it was time to think of home - home to civilisation, to mirror and glass, gleaming pavements, glistening river. Her father cried openly and declared himself unable to make the trip to the airport. He arranged for the nearest neighbour to drop her off. Thomas arrived early for her and quietly loaded up her luggage, then leaned against the car as she said her goodbyes.

He had dark curly hair and a neat beard, and he smiled and nodded at her and then leaned back to wait patiently. She was flustered as her father wept and this stranger watched, and, as she finally broke from his embrace and spun round to dash into the car, the rough laneway caught her high heels and she fell down onto her knees.

She knew she had bloodied them, but under the gaze of the pair of them she was embarrassed. It was not a graceful goodbye. She brushed off the outstretched hand and put her head down and into the car.

Silence for the first ten minutes. She looked out at the green fields and new motorways and felt the tears sting. She would miss these gentle sights. These fields had nestled into a corner of her heart, the vivid green had rested her eyes, had soothed her mind. How could she be sad saying goodbye to that which was not her home?

Why would she have this pain in her heart leaving that which was her father's dream, not her own?

"Tricky yokes, shoes," Thomas said.

She didn't reply. She hardly knew what he meant, much less what to say in return. He talked on, gently and with no urgency about the work her father was doing and how great it was to see an American with such love for the land. His voice soothed her, but she was in no mood to talk.

She stared glumly out the window until green field turned to silver terminal, turned to grey cloud.

The winter in Chicago was even colder than usual. She thought that every winter as she burrowed in her apartment to keep warm. She was sick and tired of the hardship of winter, tired of the icy wind cutting into her. She thought with fondness of the drizzle in Ireland. But for now there would be no runs along the lake for her, no strolling around farmers' markets in Lincoln Park, no dreaming Oak Park living, just her small apartment and her books.

No more architect lecturing her on light and space either. "He talked himself out of that job," her father laughed, and it was true.

All the talking, the lecturing, those opinions, the hipster clothes, the fussing over every small detail. "It's not me, it's you," she had said.Well, o.k., no, she had thought it, but had kept it quiet.

When the snow and ice thawed, she thought of another trip to the old country, as the old ones called it. Let's see how the born-again farmer is getting on, she thought. Her father was thrilled with her surprise visit, insisting on going straight to the cottage.'The old pile of stones?" she laughed. "That place has taken half a century to fall down. You bet it can wait until tomorrow." But he insisted. "You have to see what we've been doing, and we've been busy."

She borrowed some wellies and they waited for the shower to ease. They traipsed over the wet grass together. Over two fields, through a gap, then down into a dip and hidden by the grove of trees, she saw, well, the cutest darn cottage that ever hugged the ground. Fresh, white-washed walls, a red door, and slates repositioned and proud; cute little windows, winking out from the low roof. The trees cut the wind and, as they approached, the air was damp and calm.

He took out an old-fashioned key, heavy and clunky, and opened the door. They ducked in to enter, and her eyes adjusted to the light. The house was warm, its flagstones polished and sleek, the air fresh and hung with the scent of flowers. He had a table and chairs, a dresser, and there, the cup.

"Tah dah," her father announced grandly as he pulled open the yellow curtains and the room filled with a warm glow. "I'll put on the kettle and give you that cup of tea as promised."

She was speechless. He had said oftentimes that he was "working away" on the cottage, but this? She sat at the table and took it in.

He sat opposite her, he took her hands and his voice trembled. "This work has been a real pleasure for me, daughter dear. I came over here every day, rain or fine, and worked with my hands. I pulled at the roots, I dug the earth, I'm creating something here, Grainne. I'm taking the past, those tough years, and repairing the damage. The past gets filtered through with the earth in my hands. It mixes with my hopes for the future and it's good, hard, honest work."

She fought back tears, and squeezed his rough hands. "You brought it back to life, Daddy, you made it a home again."

"Oh, I couldn't have done it without Thomas. He did most of the plumbing and the wiring, and he was here nearly as many days as I was. He was great company to have around, and you just couldn't meet a better man, Grainne. He's quiet and kind and a powerful worker. He knows how good you were to me when your Mom died and how much I miss you, and he's been dying to meet you again. He's just finishing up the wall on the back."

She rose to look out into the small rear yard where he had indicated. There was Thomas, his back to them, placing the last few stones in place. She watched him carefully select the stone, turning it over in his hands, considering its rightful placement.

He turned to see her there and his face broke into a smile. He stopped and looked at her for a long moment, then turned to tend to the stone once more.

"Molann an obair an fear,"her father said softly. "The work praises the man."

When last here, she hadn't known why she was standing in the long grass looking at this ruined cottage. But now?

She knew. She knew what she was looking at. And she knew that this was for her. This was exactly what she deserved, and what she wanted - a good, strong, quiet man working out in the yard, yes even in the rain. She would watch him from the window. She would catch a wriggling child and pop it onto her lap. She could feel the child on her hip even now. She felt an atavistic yearning so deep she knew this was not someone else's dream, not just her father's, but now her own. She would live this life, away from civilisation, tucked away here in peace and quiet.

She knew what she was looking at. Her future.

AINE

By Mary Dwyer,
Glasnevin, Dublin

*Aine was the girl my son had proposed to and had been accepted by
years and years earlier. Well I remember the day he came home and
told me all about it*

RECENTLY WE WERE invited to a neighbour's 80th
birthday. He and his family live across the road from
us and have done so for almost half a century. When
we came to live here, we were either newly-weds or had young
families. It is a small cul-de-sac and an ideal place for children.

Sometimes in the summer there could be twenty or thirty
children out playing at the one time. The sounds were
delightful, lots of laughter, squeals of delight, the odd squabble
and frequent visits from Mr. Whippy.

Gradually, all that changed. Children grew up, left home,
some emigrated, some got married and they only returned for
visits. In time, we became the older generation and our cul-de-
sac a different sort of place.

But on this lovely Sunday afternoon we crossed the road to
the party. The door was open. One of the daughters greeted
us and immediately took a photo of us for their montage. The
house was packed with family, friends and relations, ranging in
ages from toddlers to octogenarians. The party spilled out into
the garden.

We were introduced to a few people and then seats were
found for us. Drinks and food were handed to us, and soon we
sat busily munching.

As I sat there quietly watching the guests, Aine, one of
the daughters, came around with more food. I never had

a conversation with her and, apart from a wave and a "hi" whenever I saw her in the distance, I did not know her at all. But for some reason, today I had a very strong urge to speak to her. Before I had time to think, I beckoned to her.

She came across to me and I heard myself saying: "Aine, could I talk to you for a few minutes when you are not so busy?"

Aine was the girl my son had proposed to and had been accepted by years and years earlier.

Well I remember the day he came home and told me all about it.

"Mam, I am going to marry Aine. I asked her and she said 'yes', and Mam, every day we will drive up to visit you and Aine's Mam, because you will be our children's grannies."

Just to make conversation, I asked where would he leave his car, our side or across the road.

He gave me a look of derision. "Mam, I won't have a car, I'll have a covered wagon and two horses."

At that time, my son was three and a half years old and Aine was two years older. All that summer I noticed that Aine had become his favourite playmate.

One of my lasting memories is of the pair of them on a sturdy little three-wheel bike, one pedalling furiously and the other standing up on the back, flying around the footpath singing at the top of their voices:

"Here comes the Wagon, Wanderly, Wanderly Wagon."

Aine came over and sat down beside me.

"Aine, do you remember little Rory?"

She looked straight into my face and said: "I remember him very well. I'll never forget the day I came home from school and my Mam told me Rory had died."

She pointed towards the window. "There was a settee there and I crept behind it and wouldn't come out for ages."

I'm not sure if she remembered the proposal, but I reminded her of it. We talked for a while and when I was leaving the party, Aine's mother told me that Aine had been broken-hearted when Rory died.

I went back across the road and for about a week my son's little face was in front of me. I felt close to him.

Rory had started so many sentences with "When I grow up."

"When I grow up, I am going to be a doctor. When I grow up, I am going to build a hospital on Ballymun Avenue and Fiona (his baby sister) will be the nurse."

The last time he used the phrase was the day before he went into hospital. This was five days before his unexpected death.

"When I grow up, I am going to buy you a ladder, up, up, up to the sky."

Then as an afterthought: "And a trap for catching lions in the garden."

"That'll be great," I said.

"When I grow up, when I grow up ..."

All the other children on our road have long since grown up, except for "little" Rory.

Robert Service in his lovely poem "The Other One" describes it so well:

"The one who will never grow up at all,
Who will always be just a child at play,
Tender and trusting and sweet and small,
Who will never leave me and go away."

I pray that my memory of him will never leave me.

ORIGINAL WRITING

FROM

IRELAND'S OWN

If you have enjoyed this collection of short stories and memoirs, and would like some more, we have some copies left of our previous publications for 2012, 2011 and 2010 at just €10 per copy, post and packing included.

2010

2011

2012

Contact:
Garrett Bonner, Original Writing, SPADE Enterprise Centre, North King Street, Dublin 7.
T - 01-6174834 • E - info@originalwriting.ie • W - www.originalwriting.ie